The controls are set, the i_____
ing; the pilot _____
maw of a thun_____
now at the merc_____
nificent, terrifyi_____

The missions ac_____ in the Thunderstorm Project and National Severe Storms
Project by the courageous pilots of the U.S.
Weather Bureau have uncovered vital new information about the nature of the thunderstorm.

Louis J. Battan, a meteorologist who has been
associated with research on thunderstorms for
more than fifteen years, describes what science
has learned about storm-generating clouds
and winds, about thunder, lightning, rain, and
hail. He details the latest experiments in
weather control such as cloud seeding and
high-altitude rocket explosion. He describes
the cumulus congestus clouds of the "local"
storm; the jet-winds that sweep the "severe"
storm on a path of destruction.

Thunderstorms are an awesome spectacle.
This book shows that we are beginning to
understand what they are, how they are formed,
and why they occur.

Other Science Books of Special Interest

The Thunderstorm

LOUIS J. BATTAN

A SIGNET SCIENCE LIBRARY BOOK

Published by THE NEW AMERICAN LIBRARY
of CANADA LIMITED

PREFACE

It is probably safe to say that since the first flicker of life on earth, thunderstorms have been a source of wonderment. By the rain they produce, plants are nourished in their growth. Sometimes, of course, the same plants are destroyed during brief periods of violent winds, torrential rain, or heavy hail. Explosive thunder can frighten the young and timid. Lightning can burn forests and houses, kill humans and animals.

Philosophers and scientists over the centuries have tried to understand the thunderstorm and the weather it produces. Except for some widely separated bursts of genius—the study of lightning by Benjamin Franklin was one—not much was learned about thunderstorms until about 30 years ago. The greatest advances in our knowledge have been made since World War II. The introduction of modern electronic equipment such as radar and the expanded use of airplanes has made it possible to obtain the kind of measurements needed to describe the thunderstorm.

The continued development of all types of electronic devices makes the future of research on thunderstorms and all other atmospheric systems a bright one. Today weather satellites are almost commonplace. They no longer are regarded with awe. But they are supplying unique observations never before available. High-speed electronic computers make it possible to analyze huge quantities of observations in reasonable time. They also allow the easy solution of the complex equations describing motions in the atmosphere.

All these factors have contributed to the rapid advancement of the atmospheric sciences. We should point out, however, that this would not have been possible without the dedicated efforts of the people who have studied the atmosphere in search of new knowledge. It is a fertile ground, indeed. For those who prefer relatively unspoiled regions, the atmospheres of the other planets are waiting to be examined.

In this small book, we have given a description of the thunderstorm—just one atmospheric phenomenon. The techniques employed to study this storm and the theories for explaining the observations are discussed briefly. It will be very obvious that quite a few of the properties of thunderstorms still are not adequately understood. It is hoped that a view of the problem will stimulate young men and women to take up careers in the atmospheric sciences and meet the challenge to find the answers.

Louis J. Battan

University of Arizona

CONTENTS

1

FLIGHT INTO
A THUNDERSTORM

Everyone's life is full of important events, but today's aims usually seem greater than yesterday's deeds. We find that time is a very coarse filter. Many ideas and remembrances slip through into the forgotten or almost forgotten. What would you say if someone said, "Quickly, tell me something important that happened to you during the year 1955." Most of us would be stuck for an answer.

As the years slip by, the human memory tends to discard the less important. Only a relatively few experiences are stamped on it forever, ready to be recalled in an instant. On August 5, 1947, a small group of us at an airbase in southwestern Ohio had such an experience. We will never forget it.

The day started out like so many others during a typical summer in the midwestern United States. It was a little hotter and somewhat more humid than a city man might have liked, but it was good for the corn growing tall and straight. Before noon, clouds started to form and showed the promise of rain. Yes, the farmers had reasons to be happy.

At Clinton County Air Force Base just outside the town of Xenia, a different breed of men also surveyed the sky with satisfaction. They were proud young men with pilot's wings hanging loosely on well-worn flight suits.

Sleek, black, twin-tailed P-61 airplanes—the Black Widows of World War II fame—were parked along the flight line. They no longer carried machine guns and other wartime gear. These had been stripped out and replaced with equipment for probing the secrets of a different kind of enemy—the thunderstorm.

From the early days of aviation, thunderstorms have been the most feared of clouds. Airplanes unfortunate enough to venture into a severe thunderhead sometimes came out one piece at a time. The violent air motions could shake even the bravest of the brave. Then there were the hazards of lightning and hail.

As the number of airplanes increased, the importance of knowing more about thunderstorms reached the point where something had to be done. Many vital questions needed answers. How strong were the air currents? How strong would airplanes have to be to survive the most severe turbulence? What was the best altitude for penetrating a storm? How could you avoid the region of most turbulence? How should you fly if you found yourself in the middle of a thunderstorm?

Pilots, airplane designers, and manufacturers needed answers to these questions. They turned to meteorologists for advice and found them asking the same questions and many others besides. What causes thunderstorms to form on some days while on others only small clouds appear? What is the source of energy for the violent air motions? Why do storms form when and where they do? To what altitudes do thunderstorms penetrate? What causes lightning and hail? The list was a long one.

Of course, thunderstorms and the violent weather they produce have had the passing attention of brilliant minds for over 2,000 years. For the most part, the attention was directed from the ground. People looked and learned. By and by, they began to climb to the tops of mountains to get a better look. Then they started sending up kites to learn about the electrical properties of storms. All these efforts yielded some new ideas. But they were just the beginning.

By the time of the twentieth century, scientists

in many countries were beginning to look at thunderstorms more critically. Not only were they concerned with what caused lightning, but what caused the storm in the first place.

The advent of aviation led to a call for improved knowledge of thunderstorms. Pilots and airplanes were being lost. Airplanes parked on landing strips were seriously damaged by strong, gusty winds.

During the thirties, a device called the "radiosonde" was developed to the point that it was adopted by the weather services. A small instrument capable of measuring temperature, humidity, and pressure was tied to a balloon and released. As the package climbed into the atmosphere, a miniature radio transmitter sent back the weather information. The radiosonde led to a surge forward in meteorology.

Instruments at the ground measured conditions under storms. Radiosondes measured temperature and humidity around them. Sometimes a balloon would even enter a thunderstorm, and thus something could be learned about the air motions within storms. But such an event was rare, and little was being learned about the structure of the thunderstorm.

The second major catastrophe of the century, World War II, found the thunderstorm still a mystery.

During 1943 and 1944, aviation and weather authorities in the United States, appalled by the still sad state of knowledge of thunderstorms, pressed for new and drastic action. The number of military and commercial aircraft lost to the fury of thunderstorms continued to mount. Finally, the pressure built up to the point where positive steps were taken. By the spring of 1945, the final decision was made to launch a major research project. All agencies in the United States with interests in aviation supported the plan. The U. S. Weather Bureau was chosen to organize the operation. The Air Force, the Navy, and several other government agencies agreed to give all necessary support.

The first major step was the appointment of Horace R. Byers as director of the entire operation. Dr. Byers, professor of meteorology at the University of Chicago, was one of the pioneers of aviation meteorology and had seen firsthand the destructive effects of thunderstorms. For many years, he had argued and pleaded for a research effort befitting the magnitude of the problem.

Dr. Byers, with the assistance of L. P. Harrison of the U. S. Weather Bureau and other advisers, formulated a plan that was ambitious and daring. It included an extensive network of observing instruments. A large number of trained people would be needed to install and operate them. These devices would shed light on the atmospheric properties in and around thunderstorms, but still they would fall short of giving the kind of information the aviation experts desperately needed. They wanted to know about turbulence within the clouds.

But how can you measure the turbulence itself? How can you find out how often it is severe enough to rip the wings off an airplane? That question was a rough one. In 1945, the inside of a thunderstorm was still a great unknown. Sometimes, airplanes flew through with just a few bumps, but at other times the results were tragic. This was a place where courage was needed. Human lives were at stake, as well as, to a certain extent, the future of aviation.

All the facts were gathered, the advice of aviation and weather experts was sought, and the decision was made: Fly into the thunderstorms, all kinds of thunderstorms, not only the weak ones whose tops extend from 25,000 to 30,000 feet but also the monsters that penetrate into the base of the stratosphere at altitudes near 50,000 feet.

Some people wondered, "Is this necessary? Do you have to jump in the oven to find out how hot it is?"

In the case of thunderstorm turbulence, the answer was, and is, a definite yes. Not only is it necessary to go in with an airplane, but you have to do it many times. Of course, the proper type of airplane must be used, equipped with special measuring equipment. More important, it is imperative that the pilots be highly skilled and experienced.

By the summer, 1945, definite plans existed in the minds of the project scientists and on paper. The next step was to find and bring together large numbers of skilled weather observers, technicians and scientists, equipment, airplanes, and, finally, pilots.

In the spring of 1945, Congress had appropriated funds to the Weather Bureau to start the research program in July. Then fate intervened in an extremely fortunate way. On August 16, 1945, a momentous day in the lives of more than half of the world, World War II came to an end. The joy of peace was doubly sweet to Dr. Byers and all the people involved in what had been named the "Thunderstorm Project." From all corners of the globe, meteorologists, technicians, weather observers, and radar experts came home looking for something worthwhile to do. They were mostly young men in their twenties, full of ambition. From this group of veterans, the nucleus of the Thunderstorm Project was formed.

Of course, the termination of the war also meant that many types of weather instruments could now be assembled from items either in the United States or overseas. The most critical items to be selected were the airplanes. Since the Air Force had assumed the responsibility of carrying out the flights through thunderstorms, the judgment of responsible officers was weighed heavily.

It was decided that because of the hazards involved, a fairly small airplane carrying only a pilot and 1 or 2 others was most desirable. Initial plans called for a crew consisting of a pilot and one man to operate a radar set and other specialized instruments. The airplane had to be capable of sustaining excessive stresses on its structure and of operating at altitudes of over 25,000 feet. It also had to be able to climb rapidly.

Study of available airplanes convinced Dr. Byers and the Air Force authorities that the P-61, the night-fighter aircraft known as the Black Widow, would do the job satisfactorily. It had been used in weather-reconnaissance work, and a reasonable number of them were available. The Air Force supplied ten airplanes. It was planned to use five on each flight. They were to be flown through thunderstorms stacked at altitude intervals of 5,000 feet.

Next came the problem of finding pilots who were prepared to fly through the heart of violent thunderstorms day after day. They had to be not only willing, but

13

able. A great deal depended on them. Fortunately for science, the young men and women of every age have courage to spare. There was no difficulty in finding competent pilots, just as there has been no difficulty in finding astronauts. When we are ready to fly to the moon or the planet Venus, there will be men and women ready to go. Furthermore, among these young people will be many ideally suited for the job—intelligent, healthy, strong in body and mind, and confident of their own abilities and the value of the undertaking.

The Air Force asked for volunteers from among their most highly rated instrument pilots. The response was immediate. A group of first-rate pilots and crews was assembled. The pilots were men with extensive experience in all types of weather; most of them had served as instrument flight instructors.

By the spring of 1946, the Thunderstorm Project had amassed a formidable group of talented people and a huge quantity of equipment. It was decided that two periods of field operations would be needed. The first would concentrate on summer thunderstorms in Florida. Since the Air Force base at Orlando, Florida, had the facilities needed for the research program, it was chosen as the location for the 1946 operation. The following year Clinton Air Force Base in southwestern Ohio served as the base of operation. A measure of the scale of the operation is shown by the fact that 22 railroad cars were needed to transport the equipment from Florida to Ohio—and this did not include trucks, jeeps, and semitrailers holding radar equipment.

We shall discuss various aspects of both the Florida and Ohio programs in later chapters, but let me skip over many aspects of the research program and take you back to August 5, 1947.

Thunderstorm Project flight procedures

By early August of 1947, the flight procedures of the project's P-61's were well established. Throughout the preceding summer, various different flight patterns had been tried. All the tests were concerned with securing the

14

best possible information about air motions and temperatures inside thunderstorms.

Various instruments had been developed or procured for installation on the airplanes. A specially designed thermometer was installed in a housing located on the top of the fuselage. The actual sensing element was a small device whose electrical resistance changed as the temperature changed. Once properly set, it worked automatically.

In the case of air motions, the airplane itself was the sensing element. The movement of the air was measured by recording the movement of the airplane. Updrafts carried it upward, downdrafts carried it downward. One might say that the airplane was like a cork in a river. By watching the cork you could see the motion of the water. The analogy has some truth, but, of course, there is one big difference: An airplane has an engine that acts to pull it through the moving air. This fact complicates the measurements somewhat.

Consider a ball that is falling in still air at 10 mph. If you were standing on the ground, it would be approaching at 10 mph. Now let us say you had a large fan pointed straight up in the air. You turn it on, and it blows air upward at exactly 10 mph. What happens? Clearly, the ball slows down until it becomes suspended in the air. It continues falling through the air at 10 mph, but the air rises at the same speed. From your vantage point on the ground, the ball stays at the same altitude.

Let us approach the problem from the other direction. One day you look out the window and see the same old ball floating in the air. Since you know that in still air the ball would fall at 10 mph, you correctly conclude that the air is rising at 10 mph.

This example is intended to demonstrate that when an airplane is used to measure air motions, it is desirable to know how it would be moving if the air were still. There is an alternative approach. In the case of thunderstorms, the primary interest is in the vertical air motions. If the airplane is flown so that its nose-to-tail axis is horizontal, the propeller will pull it neither up nor down. This was the procedure adopted.

Before heading into a thunderstorm, the pilot

15

leveled out his airplane and adjusted the controls so as to assure safe speeds. Usually the airplane slowed down below normal cruising speed. When this was done, the pilot was supposed to keep his hands off the controls. "If the ship goes up, let it go up," said the instructions; "if it goes down, let it go down."

Of course, there were limits to how far the pilots allowed the airplane to go. If a wing suddenly fell down to an excessive angle, some corrective action would have to be taken. Or if the treetops were near, it was allowable to pull back on the stick. But for the most part, the rule was "Hands off!"

In order to insure a minimum of control, a camera had been installed in the pilot's compartment during the 1946 season. It was intended to "keep the pilots honest," as the saying goes. On a number of flights, however, the pilot's shoulder or head managed to get in front of the lens. By the 1947 season, a new scheme was devised for recording how each pilot handled his airplane. All the control cables were wired to a recorder. Whenever the pilot moved the rudders or the stick, these actions were indicated by lines on a strip of film.

The pilots were sensitive to the importance of letting the airplane fly itself. By the middle of the Ohio period, they were truly veterans of thunderstorm flying. They had been through turbulence so often that they took a sudden drop of 1,000 or 2,000 feet as a matter of course. Lightning strikes and the bombardment of hail were not uncommon. The radios carried a constant chatter of Air Force slang. Perhaps the boys were becoming numb from the constant pounding. No, that wasn't it at all. They had become the best rough-weather fliers in the business. They knew it and were proud.

Sometimes, though, they were shaken. On one flight, an airplane flying at 15,000 feet in a huge, dark thunderstorm was struck by lightning. When the pilot's eyes cleared, he saw that the airspeed indicator registered 350 mph (normal speed was about 180). For an instant, panic struck. Was the airplane in a nosedive? What else could push the airspeed up so high?

The instinctive action would be to yank back on the stick, raise the nose. But experience paid off. Before

16

yielding to instinct, the pilot looked at the other instruments and believed them. They said he was flying normally. He held on and waited to break into the clear. Sure enough, when he hit clear sky he was straight and level. Something was wrong with the airspeed indicator, but what could it be and how should he land? That was easy. Another P-61 was vectored to his side by a radar controller who was directing the flight. The airplane with the faulty indicator followed his buddy who read his airspeed over the radio. They flew formation practically to the point of touchdown on the runway.

Just seconds after bringing the airplane to a stop, the mystery was solved. The lightning stroke had hit his Pitot tube, the device that serves to measure airspeed. It had melted and fused the tube shut. The intense heat built up a high pressure inside the fused section. Since the indicated airspeed increases as the pressure in the tube increases, the reason the indicator read 350 was clear. A new tube was installed, and both airplane and crew were ready to go again.

The mighty jolt

On August 5, 1947, the flight was one that even an experienced pilot could not handle. Everything started out well. Five airplanes were in flying condition, and at about 12:30 P.M. they started taking off. The low airplane was assigned to fly at 6,000 feet, the top airplane at 25,000 feet.

Each airplane carried a pilot, radar operator, and weather observer. As they climbed, the pilots called the radar control room for instructions. All the flights were directed by a chief controller, who sat in front of a radarscope in a large, darkened quonset hut about 14 miles from the airfield.

In addition to the radarscope used by the chief controller, there were several others in operation. On one was located an automatic camera, which clicked noisily away. On the scope the radar echoes from rain showers and thunderstorms appeared as bright splotches. They were getting brighter and larger.

17

The minutes ticked away as the airplanes climbed. Air Force technicians made their final checks on the radar gear. Civilian scientists checked the camera and film supply and kept their eyes on the developing weather echoes. Finally, the pilots began to call in. They had all reached assigned altitudes and were ready to go. A promising group of thunderstorms was beginning to develop about 30 miles to the west. The controller gave his instructions in a calm, steady voice,

"Three-five-three, make a thirty-degree turn to the left."

"Roger, three-five-three!"

"Three-five-six, hold your present course."

"Roger, three-five-six!"

"Three-five-four, now a right turn and hold a course of three-six-zero."

"Wilco!"

Instructions went out to all the airplanes. On the scopes, you could see little bright dots, the reflections of the airplanes, moving in response to the commands. In a matter of about 5 minutes, they were all lined up and heading for a thunderstorm.

"Hold your present headings. You're on your way in. Turn your cameras on."

In the air, the pilots saw a huge cloud towering far above them. They tightened their seat belts. Airspeed was set at about 180 mph. The airplanes were trimmed and flying straight and level. Now it was time to let go of the controls and turn the cork loose.

As airplane 354 went through the edge of the clouds at 15,000 feet, it started to shake. Ice particles started to hit the ship. A lightning bolt flashed close by, and ice began to form on the tail and wings. Then there was a heavy bump, heavy rain, heavy turbulence. Suddenly, there was an updraft. The airplane was going up. A mixture of rain and snow hit the window. Just as the altimeter hit 16,500 feet, the plane broke into the clear.

"Control, three-five-four in the clear." The time was 1:34 P.M.; the entire traverse took 4 minutes, 5 seconds.

The other airplanes also broke out at about the same time. All experienced some severe turbulence, but nothing very unusual.

18

The same procedure was repeated. After the first few runs, the two top airplanes developed engine troubles and returned to the base. The flight was continued with airplanes at 6,000, 10,000, and 15,000 feet. On board the aircraft, camera and other devices were recording the scientific data that would answer many vital questions.

The flights were rough and seemed routine, but they were harvesting information of great value.

Suddenly, on run number 7, they were no longer routine.

Over the loudspeaker came a loud, frightening call that chilled everyone in the room.

"Control! Control! This is three-five-four. Get me out of this, Control!"

The pilot's voice was shaking with terror.

"Control, I can't control the airplane! This is three-five-four. I can't control the airplane! Get me out!"

"Three-five-four, this is Control. Steer right to two-seven-zero degrees."

"Control, three-five-four, I can't turn! I can't turn it!"

"Three-five-four, okay, continue on your present heading. You should break out."

A few seconds passed by in silence. Everyone wondered, "What's going on up there?" but no one said anything. Everyone waited for another call.

Then calm voices came over the speaker.

"Control. This is three-five-three. Where's three-five-four?"

"Three-five-three, Control. Make a turn to the left to one-five-zero degrees."

"Three-five-six, Control. Roll out on one-eight-zero."

The controller was moving the other airplanes out of the way.

"Three-five-four, this is Control. Do you read?"

No answer. More seconds slipped by.

In the control room, the silence was broken only by the steady clicking of the cameras. Everyone had his eyes glued to the scope, watching the tiny dot moving slowly through the large thunderstorm. But it wasn't just a dot produced by a stream of electrons bombarding a

19

glass face coated with phosphor. That dot was 3 men riding in a tin can out of control.

"Click, Click, Click. . . ." The cameras went on. Science was still on the march.

As suddenly as it had started, it was over.

"Control, three-five-four. I'm okay at ten thousand feet."

In the control room, they didn't cheer. It was more like a sigh or a groan—a mixture of profanity and prayer. Everyone had forgotten how hot it was, but everyone was soaked with perspiration. But who cared? They were in the clear.

Then came another call, "Control, three-five-four. Correction. That altitude is twenty thousand feet!"

"Come on home, three-five-four."

Postflight briefing

Immediately after each flight, the crews were briefed by Thunderstorm Project scientists. Most of the questions came from Roscoe R. Braham, Jr., Richard D. Coons, and Fred White,* the men who were Dr. Byers' chief assistants. From notes and transcriptions of the day's flights, each thunderstorm penetration was discussed. It was important to do this as quickly as possible, while the details were still fresh in the minds of everyone.

The same type of postflight briefing has been used with the astronauts. As soon as they can be plucked from the capsule, they are rushed to an interrogation room. They are questioned by a battery of scientists about what they saw, felt, smelled, heard, and so on. Sometimes, by sifting many seemingly unrelated and inconsequential items of information, an important idea or fact may emerge.

The meeting with the crews who flew on August 5,

---

* Braham is now associate professor of meteorology at the University of Chicago. Coons is a vice-president of Geophysics Corporation of America in Boston. White is associated with the National Science Foundation in Washington, D.C.

1947, was not the same as so many others before and after it. An airplane almost hadn't made it back that day—that was the thought foremost in the minds of everyone in the room. Braham, Coons, and White were just as anxious as the others to get all the facts and details about 354's mighty jolt. But it was also important to get all the details about the other penetrations and the other airplanes. They started from the beginning.

What happened on the first pass? How severe was the turbulence? Was it the same on the whole run through the cloud? Was there any turbulence in the clear air on either side of the cloud? How much altitude was gained or lost? Was there rain or snow? Was there any hail? How large were the stones? How about icing? How thick was it? On and on went the questioning.

It is true that many of these questions would be answered when the films and other records were analyzed. But double checks were essential. Also, an important part of the research program was to test pilots' reaction to severe weather. A pilot's judgment as to the severity of turbulence changes with experience. How he feels at the time, physically and mentally, affects his decisions. The instruments measured the turbulence, but only an analysis of the pilot's reaction would tell about him.

Finally, the time came for the pilot of 354 to describe the pass we would never forget.

Until that last penetration everything had been fairly routine. On most runs there were patches of severe turbulence with losses or gains of up to 2,000 feet on each one. As he headed into the last cloud, there was no indication that this pass would be any different than the rest.

Then, suddenly, very severe turbulence was encountered. It was just like hitting a brick wall! The airplane went completely out of control. Pulling the stick, pushing the rudders did nothing. There was heavy rain and snow throughout, and heavy hail in the last 40 seconds. Lightning flashes were too numerous to count. Visibility was reduced to inches. The air was carrying the airplane either up or down—the pilot didn't know which. The notes showed the air was going up. The

21

airplane went from 15,000 to 20,000 feet in *one minute*.

In the control room, it seemed that the pass took a long time, but the clocks showed otherwise. Almost exactly a minute elapsed from the time the pilot called for help to the time he broke into the clear. Later examinations of the films of the altimeter showed that the airplane entered the cloud at 15,000 feet. Quite suddenly it started gaining altitude, and it reached 20,000 feet after a minute. Thus, the plane was being lifted at a speed of 5,000 ft/min, or about 57 mph—a mighty powerful updraft, indeed.

An interesting fact was dramatized by this flight. Three airplanes entered the same cloud. The one at 15,000 feet encountered extremely severe turbulence. But the other two, one 5,000 feet below and the other 9,000 feet below, did not suffer such severe turbulence. As a matter of fact, the airplane at 10,000 feet reported no updrafts or downdrafts of consequence. Why? This was a question of paramount importance. Was the updraft composed of a very narrow core that was missed by the lower airplanes? It is true that the controller tried to line up the planes before entry, but it is equally true that they could have been more than 1,000 feet out of line. Also, the updraft might have been tilted instead of straight up and down.

There is another possible explanation. Is it possible that the updraft, rather than being in the form of a long vertical column, was made up of "bubbles" of air rising rapidly through the cloud? Perhaps 354 went through the center of a large bubble while the others flew through the slow-moving air surrounding it.

One of the chief reasons for setting up the Thunderstorm Project was to learn about the air motions in thunderstorms. A great deal was learned. Some important questions were given satisfactory answers. Others could not be resolved. In some cases, the findings of the project led to more questions rather than answers.

Over the last 15 years, meteorologists have continued the study of thunderstorms. In the following chapters, we shall discuss what has been learned. Lest anyone get the impression that all the problems have been solved, we should mention at the outset that this is certainly not the case. Gaps in our knowledge will be pointed out in the appropriate places. Scientists all over the world are working to bridge them.

2

WHY THUNDERSTORMS?

Are thunderstorms necessary?

You might say that it depends on who you are and what you do. When a loud clap of thunder in the middle of the night awakens the baby and turns a peaceful sleep into an hour of sobs and tears, a mother's reaction is predictable. A pilot caught in a thunderstorm might agree with the mother. A farmer watching hail beat a field of wheat into the ground might also curse the weather gods. On the other hand, on another day, the same farmer seeing a thunderstorm wet down a parched field of corn would be a happy man. These, and other human reactions, are easily understood, but they do not give a satisfactory answer to our question.

In order to know if thunderstorms are necessary, we should ask why they form. Is it possible that they affect us all in ways we might not even suspect?

In 1925, C. E. P. Brooks in England made an extensive study of the climatological records and concluded that, at all times, an average of 1,800 thunderstorms are in progress over the earth. Other scientists have proposed that a more realistic estimate may be two or three times higher, but let us stick with Brooks' number. It may seem large, but it must be realized that between the latitude circles 30°N and 30°S thunderstorms are quite common.

An individual storm lasts for about an hour or so. It is clear that in order for 1,800 to be in existence at all times, new ones must be constantly forming to take the place of the ones dying out. As the storms form and dissipate, they accomplish several important functions. First of all, they transport energy from low levels of the atmosphere to high levels. They also transport other things —electric charge, for example.

Let us examine why and how thunderstorms carry energy from regions where there is a great deal to regions where there is little.

Thunderstorms transport energy

On a typical summer day, a great deal of heat reaches the ground and the low layers of the atmosphere in the form of radiation from the sun. As more and more solar energy is absorbed by the ground and the moist air near it, the temperature rises. When this occurs, the surface of the earth and the water vapor in the air begin to re-radiate increasing quantities of heat, but the amount that escapes into outer space still is much smaller than the amount coming in from the sun. The air in the upper layers of the atmosphere absorbs little radiation either from the sun or from the lower regions. As a result, the low layers of the atmosphere tend to get warmer and warmer, while the upper layers change but little.

If radiation were the only mechanism for the transfer of heat, life in some regions of the earth could not survive. Daytime temperatures during the summer would reach such high levels as to make life for plants and animals unbearable. Fortunately, there are other mechanisms. First, there is a process called "Molecular conduction." As the name implies, heat is transferred by the action of molecules. In a volume of warm air, the molecules are flying and bouncing around much faster than they are in a volume of cold air. As a matter of fact, physicists have shown that the temperature of any gas can be expressed in terms of the velocity of the molecules: the faster they move, the higher the temperature, and vice versa.

25

Now if two volumes of air, one warm and one cold, were suddenly placed side by side, the air molecules from the warm volume would immediately start to bombard the cold volume. Fast and slow air molecules would begin to mix and bounce off one another. As time went on, the initially cold volume would begin warming up because the air molecules of which it was composed would be speeded up. On the other hand, the volume of air that was warm at the beginning would be cooler because some of its fast-moving molecules would be replaced by slower ones. After the passage of sufficient time, the temperature of both volumes would be the same. The net result of the molecular exchanges would be a transfer of heat from the warm volume to the cold one.

As the air temperature near the earth increases with respect to that in higher layers of the atmosphere, molecular conduction begins. Heat is transferred upward. This process is slow—even with outward radiation and molecular conduction working together to carry heat away, they still cannot compensate for the constant inflow of solar energy. In order to prevent air temperatures from reaching extremely high values, another transfer mechanism is needed. That mechanism is known as "convection."

When a meteorologist uses the term "convection," he refers to the motions of a fluid that result in the transport and mixing of the properties of the fluid. Usually the motions are upward and downward. Convective currents solve our problem of transporting heat from the low layers of the atmosphere to the high levels.

As far back as 1885, scientists wondered about the role of convection in fluids. They studied the problem by pouring a shallow layer of fluid in a dish and warming the bottom. Tiny particles that could easily be seen were placed in the fluid so that its motion could be observed. When heat was first applied, the observers saw no motion. As the temperature at the bottom of the fluid increased, however, distinct patterns formed on the top surface. Nearly equally spaced centers of rising fluid were surrounded by larger regions of descending fluid.

We now know how to explain these experiments. When the temperature at the bottom of the fluid is only slightly higher than the temperature at the top, heat is transferred upward by molecular action. The naked eye sees nothing. As the temperature difference increases beyond a certain critical value, convection sets in. The fluid begins to move up in some regions and down in others. Mathematical equations have been derived that describe the action quite well, at least in certain specific cases. The point at which convection starts depends not only on the temperatures but on the properties of the fluid and on the shape of the vessel holding it.

The results of studies of fluid convection are important as far as the atmosphere is concerned. For most problems concerned with motions, air can be regarded as a fluid. The equations of motion of air currents and ocean currents are similar in many respects. Of course, in solving the equations it is necessary to take due notice of the fact that the physical properties of fluids and gases differ. For example, the weight of a cubic inch of air in the lower atmosphere is about 1,000 times smaller than that of water.

The results of laboratory and mathematical studies show that when the lower layers of air in the atmosphere become substantially warmer than the upper layers, convection starts. Air begins to rise, and heat is transferred upward, thereby reducing the temperature differences. Sometimes the convective currents are weak and do not penetrate very high. At other times they extend high enough into the atmosphere to lead to the formation of the white, puffy clouds often seen in the summer. Occasionally, the convective currents are very powerful, and a vertical column of air may grow to an altitude of 10 miles. When this happens, we have a thunderstorm, the largest in the family of so-called "convective clouds."

To an important extent, the depth of the convection depends on the temperature distribution in the atmosphere. As we have already noted, temperatures are normally highest near the surface, decreasing with height. The more rapid the decrease, the more likely is the occurrence of convection. For this reason, the rate of decrease is used to measure what is known as the "stability" of the atmosphere. When the temperature decreases rapidly with height, the atmosphere is said to be

27

"unstable" and the chances of strong convection and thunderstorms are good.

We noted earlier that, in order to prevent the temperature near the earth from getting too high, an efficient means for transferring heat upward is needed. Nature has supplied such a means in the form of convection. As the lower layers get increasingly hot, convection transfers increasing quantities of heat. When conditions become very unstable and drastic action is needed, the thunderstorm is waiting in the wings, ready to take to the stage.

Convection, water vapor, and energy

In the preceding section, we considered how air motions can transfer heat from low levels to high levels. The term "heat" was used to designate a form of energy that is transferred from a warm body to a cooler one. If your hand slips and hits a hot stove, heat is transferred to you and the hand gets hot. When you pick up an ice cube, heat is transferred to the ice and your hand gets cold. This form of heat transport is familiar to everyone. It is important in the atmosphere, but there is another heat-transfer process that is less well known but no less important.

Let us consider what happens when you get out of a swimming pool on a hot day. If the relative humidity of the air is very low, you feel chilled when you first step out of the water. This happens even when the temperature is more than 100°F. If the air temperature were 100°F and your body temperature was normal at 98.6°F, there would be a transfer of thermal energy from the hot air to your cooler body. This should act to warm you. However, this is more than counterbalanced by another heat-transfer mechanism. As most people know, it is associated with the familiar process of evaporation.

If you had a superpowerful magnifying glass, you would see that you become dry because water molecules fly off into the air. In order for them to do this, energy must be supplied to increase their speeds to the point that they can move away from the layer of water in

28

which they initially find themselves. The necessary energy comes from the thermal energy of the water layer and your skin. The more rapid the evaporation, the more rapid is the heat extracted and the cooler you become. Of course, when the water has evaporated, the conduction of heat from the warm air becomes dominant, and you soon become hot. At this point, you can jump back into the water again.

It has been found that a fixed quantity of heat is needed to evaporate a fixed quantity of water. When the air temperature is 0°C (32°F), you have to supply 597 calories of heat in order to evaporate 1 gram of water. When the reverse of evaporation occurs, namely condensation, heat is given off. If you have a glass of ice water on which condensation is occurring, 597 calories of heat are being supplied to the glass for every gram of water condensed. This heat helps to melt the ice.

The heat released by vaporization or condensation is called "latent heat." When you note that the term "latent" means "that which exists but is as yet unrevealed," it is clear why the name latent heat came into use. If one had a volume of air into which water is evaporated, the temperature of the air would be reduced by virtue of the evaporation. On the other hand, if condensation took place, latent heat would be released and the temperature of the air would rise.

This, perhaps excessive, introduction to the concept of latent heat has been given because of its vital importance in thunderstorms.

We noted earlier that convection transports thermal heat upward. It should now be realized that thunderstorms also transfer very large quantities of latent heat. This is the way that happens. When a warm parcel of air begins to rise and moves to higher altitudes where the pressure is lower, the air begins to expand. Energy is needed to bring about expansion. That energy comes from the air and leads to a cooling and a reduction of the air temperature. In the atmosphere, a rising parcel of air is cooled at a rate of about 5.5°F for each 1,000 feet of ascent (see Figure 1). As long as the temperature of the atmosphere decreases at a greater rate, the parcel remains warmer than the surrounding air at

29

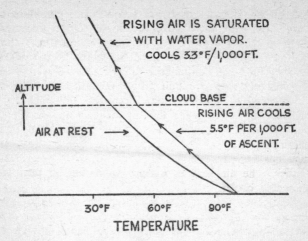

Figure 1. *A rising parcel of air cools at a rate of 5.5°F for each 1,000 feet of ascent until condensation begins at the cloud base. The released heat of condensation reduces the cooling rate as the parcel rises above the cloud base. In the case illustrated, the rising parcel remains warmer than the surrounding air at rest. As long as it is warmer, it is also lighter and is accelerated upward.*

the same altitude. In this case, it remains lighter and continues to rise. The reduction of the temperature of the air parcel causes its relative humidity to increase. When it reaches close to 100 percent, condensation begins. Cloud droplets appear. As we have already noted, this leads to a release of the latent heat of condensation. Once this starts, the temperature of the rising parcel decreases at a rate of about 3.3°F per 1,000 feet. This released heat counteracts some of the cooling caused by expansion.

If only a small cloud with very tiny droplets forms, not much latent heat is transferred. When the droplets evaporate, the heat is extracted from almost the same air to which it was added. When a heavy shower such as a thunderstorm is produced, this is no longer the case.

As the air in the rising column of air goes to higher

and higher altitudes, the water condensed combines to form large water and ice particles. When the diameters of these particles exceed a few hundred microns,* they fall out of the rising air parcel in which they formed. As they fall, they continued to grow and may even reach the ground as rain or hail. Thus, the original parcel of air warmed by condensation arrives at some high level of the atmosphere while the products of the condensation fall to the ground. They eventually evaporate and extract heat from their surroundings. In this process, heat has been transferred from low altitudes to high altitudes. The air aloft is warmer while the air near the ground is cooler.

Sometimes the particles of water and ice grow large enough to fall out of the volume of air in which they originally condensed but still are not large enough to reach the ground before evaporating. This, too, leads to a transfer of heat from one layer of the atmosphere to a higher one.

A dramatic effect of the transfer of cool air downward in a thunderstorm is supplied by the outward rush to cool air often experienced just before a thunderstorm strikes. It is caused by evaporation of water droplets in a descending current of air called the "downdraft." Sometimes the air temperature may fall by 10 or 20°F in a matter of minutes as downdraft air pushes aside the sun-warmed air near the ground. We shall discuss this feature of storms in more detail later.

At this point, it should be clear that convective clouds and thunderstorms are capable of transporting heat upward in the atmosphere. Meteorologists have established that they represent the major mechanism for accomplishing this essential function. Furthermore, in so doing, they constitute a vital part of the machinery for keeping the circulation of the atmosphere in proper balance. For these reasons, thunderstorms must be regarded as necessary parts of nature's plan.

---

* A micron is one millionth of a meter, equal to 0.000039 inches. Typical cloud droplets have diameters of about 20 microns; raindrops are often about 2,000 microns in diameter.

Before examining the details of how thunderstorms develop, let us first consider the two general types of motion in a thunderstorm.

A large thundercloud can grow at a rate of several thousand feet per minute. When you lie back in the grass on a summer's day and watch a storm cloud grow, it does not look very fast. From your vantage point, of course, you have a hard time following the turning and twisting of the cloud boundaries. If you want to get a good idea of the movement of the cloud, you can use a well-known photographic trick. Set up a movie camera and take a shot every 5 seconds. After the film has been developed, project it at perhaps 16 frames per second. This speeds up the action by 80 times. The results can be really impressive. A huge white cloud will plunge upward, its forward edge swelling and boiling. Although the top ascends fairly evenly upward, it is often seen folding into itself. The individual tufts are like cloud eddies with diameters much smaller than the climbing columns of air.

It is common to speak of the general rising body of air as the "updraft," while the smaller disturbances may be called "gusts." Measurements made inside clouds have led to the concept of drafts and gusts. One can picture what happens inside a building thunderstorm by visualizing water flowing down a river. As we all know, a river is a body of water moving downward toward the sea. Most of the water flows steadily downhill. Often, however, you see whirls superimposed on the steady stream, particularly in the vicinity of shorelines. When a boat floats down the river, it moves along smoothly so long as it stays in the steady stream. When it passes through one of the whirls or eddies, it is likely to be rocked back and forth—you might say it experiences turbulence. Clearly, the turbulence depends on the size and strength of the eddy as well as on the type and speed of the boat.

A similar situation prevails in a thunderstorm. An updraft can be considered as a fairly steady stream of rising air. If an airplane entered a pure draft, it would be carried upward but would undergo little bouncing and shaking. This almost never happens. Updrafts (and downdrafts), like rivers, are accompanied by eddies, or gusts, as they are called. As a matter of fact, the evidence indicates that the stronger the drafts, the greater the number and intensity of the eddies. These are the things that subject an airplane to turbulence.

As is the case with a boat in a stream, the degree of turbulence suffered by an airplane depends on the properties of the gusts. The important ones are those whose diameters are about as large as the wing span of the airplane. As one would expect, the stronger the eddy speeds, the more violent the effect on the airplane when it flies through one. An important fact that has long been recognized is that the faster the speed of the airplane, the more severe the turbulence it will suffer from a particular gust. Personal experiences with an automobile make it easy to remember this point. When there is a bump in the road, the "turbulence" suffered by a car is less if the bump is crossed at a low speed rather than at a high speed.

When discussing the effects of thunderstorm air motions on the flight of an airplane, the difference between drafts and gusts should be clearly understood. Also, the role of the airplane must be recognized. Aviation authorities have long recognized this point. When they speak of turbulence, they realize that it is not sufficient to refer only to the vertical force or acceleration experienced by an airplane. Instead, they have invented the "derived gust velocity," which is calculated from an equation that takes into account not only the vertical acceleration, but the characteristics of the airplane and its airspeed. The appropriate equation yields a velocity that, in theory, corresponds to the velocity of a gust that would produce an acceleration equal to the one actually experienced by the airplane. The concept of the derived gust velocity is very useful. It permits engineers to calculate the effect any particular gust would have on any airplane. The airplanes of the Thunderstorm Project were equipped to measure draft speeds and gust intensities.

Two classes of thunderstorms

Sometimes a thunderstorm forms a solitary mountain of white in a field of small, puffy clouds—a huge cauliflower in a field of mushrooms. As the churning, gleaming top plows its way deeper and deeper into the blue, the little clouds around it may disappear as if overwhelmed by the giant in their midst. As the brilliant mass reaches higher into the atmosphere, where very cold air resides, its structure begins to change. The texture of its edges changes. It becomes fuzzy and begins spreading outward under the force of strong winds. Soon an anvil forms. Sparks begin to fly, and thunder rolls.

Isolated thunderstorms that follow this script do not occur very often, but they cannot be said to be rare. When they do occur, they are thrilling to watch. Most often, thunderstorms form in groups or lines. When this occurs, you cannot see much from the ground. The sky may be pure chaos, with different types of clouds at various altitudes moving in different directions. Intense rain, lightning, thunder—perhaps even hail—can be mingled in time and space. You can say for sure that there are thunderstorms overhead, but how many are there? The human senses alone cannot give you the answer. Special types of instruments are needed for this purpose.

It has been found that even in the most seemingly confused thunderstorm, there is a considerable amount of organization. In the formation of the storm, in the updrafts and downdrafts, there is much less chaos than an observer might think.

At one time, it was felt that all thunderstorms were basically the same. They were visualized as being composed of one or more "cells," each following a fairly well-defined life cycle. It was thought that the major difference between a simple storm and a complicated one was that the latter had more cells than the former.

Over the last few years there has been growing evidence that the cellular concept is too simple. It appears to be valid in some cases but not in others. New observations and ideas indicate that the thunderstorms that produce severe weather are basically different from those giving merely some rain and the usual amount of lightning and thunder.

By severe weather we mean hail that exceeds an inch and sometimes 3 inches in diameter, winds exceeding speeds of 60 mph, and sometimes tornadoes. These thunderstorms usually are found along lines that sweep across the country. Often the lines can be followed for many hundreds of miles. They produce extensive damage to crops and property along the way. Sometimes they maim and kill as well.

The other class of thunderstorms, those that are more isolated and last for perhaps an hour or so, are easiest to study. They are often called "local storms." Of course, sometimes a single isolated thunderstorm can suddenly develop into a violent storm with torrential rain and hail. However, this type of weather is not usually expected from local showers. Let us first examine some of the characteristics of local storms. Then we shall consider the organized violent storms.

3

LOCAL THUNDERSTORMS

The essential atmospheric conditions for the formation of local thunderstorms can be simply stated. First of all, air must be moist through a fairly deep layer in the atmosphere, 10,000 feet or more. Secondly, the atmosphere should be unstable. Finally, there should be few clouds during the morning hours so that the sun's rays can heat the ground and the air near it.

In an earlier chapter, we touched on all three of these points. Let us consider them here in a little more detail.

Unstable air

To begin with, what exactly does a meteorologist mean when he says that the atmosphere is "unstable"? In the simplest terms, he means that regions of air are ready to rise to great altitudes if you give them a little push. In the same way, a large rock delicately balanced on the top of a mountain is unstable. Give it a little nudge and down it goes, rolling at ever-increasing speed, causing more rocks and stones to fall with it, perhaps even causing an avalanche.

Consider a small volume of air that is rising through an atmosphere at rest. In order for the small parcel to continue rising at ever-increasing speeds, it must be lighter than the air surrounding it. That's why a balloon filled with helium goes up. This gas is lighter than air. (More specifically, a physicist would say the "density," that is, the mass per unit volume, of helium is less than that of air.) A parcel of air will accelerate upward as long as its density is less than that of the surrounding air. Since the density of air decreases as its temperature increases, vertical acceleration continues as long as a volume of air is warmer than its surroundings.

In the atmosphere, temperature normally decreases with altitude. Instability exists when the rate of decrease is large. We already noted that rising dry air expands because it moves into regions of decreasing pressure. As a result, it cools off. The rate of cooling has been found to be about 5.5°F per 1,000 feet of ascent. This value is called the "dry-adiabatic lapse rate." * In order for a rising volume of dry air to continue accelerating, it must ascend in an atmosphere in which the temperature is decreasing more rapidly with height than 5.5°F/1,000 feet. Except near the surface of the earth, especially in desert regions, such conditions seldom exist. When they are present, many thermals, or, as the old fliers used to say, "air pockets," are produced. Airplane flights in such conditions can be unpleasant. The drafts are not particularly strong or the gusts severe, but there may be countless small ones. An airplane can be constantly bouncing and shaking.

If the atmosphere were dry to great depths, there would not be thunderstorms. Rising air cooling at the dry-adiabatic lapse rate would, after moderate amounts of ascent, reach levels where its temperature would be equal to that of the surrounding air. It would then slow down and finally stop. In such a case, the source of the energy for the rising air is inadequate to cause columns of air to penetrate to very great altitudes. Additional

---

* The term "lapse rate" comes from the fact that the temperature decreases, that is, it lapses. The word *adiabatic* indicates that the cooling is caused by internal energy changes, not by loss of heat to air outside the rising parcel. The lapse rate is called dry because all the moisture is in the form of water vapor. Once condensation begins and cloud droplets form, latent heat is released and the lapse rate changes. In such a case, it is called the "moist-adiabatic lapse rate."

37

energy besides heat near the earth's surface is needed. This is where water vapor enters the scene.

If the air is moist, another source of energy is waiting to be tapped. If the air near the ground is heated sufficiently by the sun, it may start to rise dry adiabatically in the manner already mentioned. However, instead of running out of energy as it did in the case of very dry air, the air may push high enough to reach the point where condensation begins. Once this has started, the new energy begins to be released. Latent heat is added at a rate of 597 calories per gram of water condensed.

As we noted earlier, the effect of the heat of condensation is to reduce the rate of expansion cooling from 5.5 to 3.3°F per 1,000 feet of ascent. This new lower figure is called the "moist-adiabatic lapse rate."

After condensation has started, rising air will continue accelerating upward as long as the decrease of temperature with the height of the environment exceeds the moist-adiabatic lapse rate. This condition occurs quite commonly, particularly in the spring and summer months. As a consequence, large convective clouds and thunderstorms form during these periods.

A thunderstorm grows

The normal course of events on days with local thunderstorms is to have convection build up gradually. As noon approaches and surface temperatures increase, small, puffy clouds begin to form. These small clouds called "cumulus" are very common (Plate I). At first individual clouds may last for less than five minutes. As old ones evaporate, new ones form. With the climb of the sun and the surface temperature, the comuli grow larger and last for longer periods of time.

As each cloud pokes its nose into dry air, it feels the pinch of evaporation. When it does evaporate, it leaves the air a little more moist than it was before.

Gradually the clouds in the sky become more numerous and larger. Finally, a group of them combine to form a column of rising air perhaps a mile in diameter. As long as the inner core of the column is warmer than the surrounding air, it continues to push skyward. If the temperature of the surrounding air is decreasing rapidly with height, the updraft becomes stronger. The top of the cloud rises at perhaps 1,000 to 2,000 ft/min. The cloud has a white, sharply defined appearance. At this point, it would be called a "cumulus congestus" (Plate II).

We stated earlier that in order for thunderstorms to develop, the atmosphere should be both unstable and moist. At that time it was pointed out that when the air is humid, a supply of latent heat is avilable. A high relative humidity through a deep layer of the atmosphere is important for another reason, too. When the air is humid, a growing cloud evaporates more slowly.

As the top of a cumulus congestus cloud churns its way upward into blue sky, it entraps some of the clear air through its top and sides. As the clear air mixes with cloud air, cloud droplets evaporate by the amount needed to saturate the clear air with water vapor. As we have already seen, evaporation causes the temperature to fall. This action, in turn, leads to heavier air and a slowing down of the updraft. When the air outside the cloud is close to saturation, that is, when its relative humidity is close to 100 percent, cloud-droplet evaporation is small. On the other hand, if the air surrounding the cloud is very dry (for example, if its relative humidity is 10 percent), the mixing and evaporation into the cloud can cause so much cooling that the cloud stops growing.

Let us consider the case when the air is both unstable and moist. The cumulus congestus cloud is the egg from which a thunderstorm is hatched. As the cloud air keeps pushing upward at faster and faster speeds, various important processes are at work.

First of all, the cloud droplets that first formed by condensation at the cloud base move upward with the rising air. Typical cloud droplets are only about 20 microns in diameter. In still air, they would fall at speeds of about 2 ft/min. Since the updraft speeds are 100 to 1,000 times stronger, the droplets would be carried along. As they rise to higher regions in the cloud, they continue to

39

grow. The larger ones soon begin to collide with the smaller ones. Their diameters increase rapidly. Some 20 minutes or so after the cumulus congestus started to develop, the largest droplets can be called small raindrops. Their diameters would be perhaps 100 to 200 microns.

Over the midwestern United States, cloud base heights in the summer are normally about 5,000 feet above the ground. By the time a cloud has reached about 25,000 feet, it will usually contain small raindrops in its upper regions. In another 5 minutes or so, rain will be seen falling from the cloud base. During this period, the cloud top continues to rise.

It has been found that over the Midwest in the summer, the height of the 32°F level is about 15,000 feet. This level has usually been called the "freezing level," but this convention is going slowly out of practice and it is becoming more common to call it the "melting level." The reason for this apparent quibbling with words is physically sound. When cloud droplets are carried upward through the 32°F level, they usually do not freeze. Instead, they get colder than 32°F and still remain liquid. They "supercool." Water droplets at temperatures of 0°F are often found in growing cumulus congestus clouds. Sometimes when tiny droplets are involved, cooling may extend to as low as —38° F.*

When ice crystals and snowflakes fall from the upper region of a cloud through the 32°F level, they begin to melt immediately. This is the reason why the term "melting level" is becoming more popular.

Let us get back to the building cumulus congestus. Its top has passed 25,000 feet and is still going strong. Large supercooled water drops with temperatures of 5°F are present now. Some ice crystals have formed. The rain process has begun, and so has the cloud electrification process. This phase in the growth of a thunderstorm was called the "cumulus stage" of development by scientists

---

* Some recent reports have stated that high-flying aircraft have found supercooled drops at temperatures below –58°F. These observations are contrary to results in laboratory experiments and theoretical studies. More flight observations are being made to establish if the earlier results were reliable. If they are, the current views on the freezing of droplets will have to be revised.

on the Thunderstorm Project. Figure 2 presents a simplified picture of the fields of vertical air velocities. It can be seen that a characteristic feature at this point in the cloud's history is the updraft.

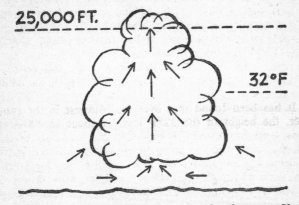

25,000 FT.

32°F

Figure 2.   *The cumulus stage of a thunderstorm. Updrafts predominate and lead to rapid growth of the cloud.*

One should not be misled into thinking that all of air is rising. In flying through a cloud such as the one pictured in Figure 2, there would be upward and downward gusts, but the average air motion would be upward. There is still uncertainty about the detailed structure of the updraft. The Thunderstorm Project pilots found that in some cumulus clouds there were updrafts at each of the levels flown. For this reason Horace R. Byers and Roscoe R. Braham, in formulating the cellular theory of thunderstorms, visualized that the updraft had somewhat the chimney appearance shown in the illustration. On the other hand, a group of English scientists, notably R. S. Scorer and F. H. Ludlam, have proposed that the updraft is composed of a series of large "bubbles" of air. In their view, the updraft would have weak and strong sections depending on whether you examined the bubble interior or its wake.

Unfortunately, we still have not obtained the kind of measurements needed to resolve the different views. The

41

flight measurements of the Thunderstorm Project for the most part supported the "column" idea, but not always. Occasionally a strong updraft was measured at one level —for example, 15,000 feet—while weak drafts were formed at a different altitude—for example, 10,000 feet. It is true that one can argue that perhaps one of the airplanes was displaced relative to the draft. Perhaps the airplane at 10,000 feet flew alongside the draft rather than through it.

One of the chief factors in support of the bubble theory is the appearance of the top of a growing convective cloud. It has a tendency to pulsate. The cloud summit does not move upward as a rigid body. Rather, different parts of it grow at slightly different rates. First, a knob on one side pushes ahead. Then it slows down and a cloud tower accelerates on the other side. It has been argued that this behavior indicates that different bubbles of air, which started near the ground, have reached the top of the cloud.

Research programs now in progress are concerned with the nature of the updraft. Some definite answers should be coming along in the next few years.

In the meantime, we have to be satisfied with the generality that the average air motion during the cumulus stage is upward. Measurements have shown that updrafts as great as 3,000 ft/min are not unusual. Since such strong drafts are usually accompanied by substantial gusts, severe turbulence can be expected by an airplane unlucky enough to blunder into one of these clouds.

At the University of Chicago, Braham calculated how much air may be carried by the updraft, making use of statistics of the Thunderstorm Project. The average updraft transports about 8,000 tons of air per second. This certainly seems like an enormous quantity of air, but when you compare it with the air transported by a large hurricane, it is quite small. We often think of air as having almost no mass at all. As a matter of fact, it is very light. Nevertheless, if you have large volumes, you have large weights.

At any rate, a tremendous quantity of air is funneled up to higher levels through a cumulus cloud. Where does it come from? Most of it originates in the layer of air close to the ground. As the updraft begins, air converges toward the cloud. The air may come from a distance many miles from the cloud. Sensitive instruments can detect the inflow toward the cloud.

As the updraft grows, it also adds to itself by drawing in air outside the cloud. Meteorologists say that the updraft "entrains" air.

As air moves up the chimney and the cloud top climbs, it pushes aside the air ahead of it, but not all of it. We mentioned earlier that there is entrainment at the top of the cloud, too. It is reasonable to ask about the fate of the air being shoved out of the way by the updraft. The answer is fairly obvious. It moves first horizontally and then begins to sink. The descent of the air takes place over an area much larger than that of the updraft.

Figure 3. *The air motion in and around a rapidly building convective cloud.*

The entire cumulus cloud system is illustrated in Figure 3. It can be seen that the air motions are similar in many respects to the convective motions in liquids that we described earlier. The convective cloud transports heat upward from the warm layers near the ground to the cooler layers aloft.

Mature stage of a thunderstorm

As the cumulus congestus cloud continues growing to greater altitudes, the updraft gets stronger and the raindrops and ice particles become larger. Soon the precipitation particles reach sizes where they can no longer be supported by the updraft, and they begin to fall rapidly toward the ground. The total weight of the rain, snow, and hail can become so large that it exerts a downward force on the air. This force can slow down the updraft. If the weight becomes large enough, a downdraft is started at some intermediate level in the cloud.

Once the downdraft starts, it accelerates very fast. As the air descends to levels where the pressure is higher, it begins to warm up because of compression. If there were no water or ice particles, the warming would amount to about $5.5°F/1,000$ feet of descent, the same value we cited earlier. However, in the thunderstorm, there is plenty of water and ice. They evaporate and cool the air, causing the rate of temperature increase to be about $3.3°F/1,000$ feet. The temperature of the environment increases downward at a greater rate. As a result, the downdraft air gets colder and heavier than the air around it and it falls rapidly toward the ground.

By the time rain begins to hit the earth, the thunderstorm contains both a downdraft and an updraft. The storm has reached its mature stage. Figure 4 illustrates the air motion at this time.

In the mature stage, the thunderstorm has reached the peak of its violent life. Updraft speeds may be spectacular. The flight discussed in Chapter 1 was through a mature storm. As you may recall, it contained an updraft of 5,000 ft/min. In the upper parts of the clouds, much stronger drafts may occur.

Mature storms may reach altitudes over 60,000 feet— the stratosphere's the limit. Large thunderstorms actually penetrate some 5,000 feet or so into the stratosphere. Unless the updrafts are very strong, they cannot go much higher. The reasons are fairly simple. By defini-

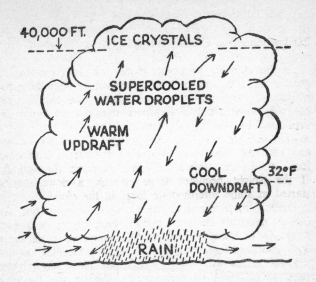

Figure 4. *The mature stage of a thunderstorm. At this time it is most violent with heavy rainfall, severe turbulence, lightning, and possibly hail.*

tion, the stratosphere begins where the temperature is either constant or increases with height for a substantial distance. Such a region is very stable. A rising parcel of air, cooling at the moist-adiabatic rate in an environment where temperature is constant with altitude, will soon find itself cooler than the environment. As a result, it will be slowed down. If, at the time the deceleration begins, the updraft has a very high speed, it can still rise many thousands of feet before it loses its upward momentum.

Vonnegut and Moore at A. D. Little, Inc., were the first to suggest a convenient rule of thumb for calculating how fast the updraft would have to be to penetrate the stratosphere. His rule is that for every 1,000 feet of penetration, the updraft speed at the base of the stratosphere would have to be about 20 ft/sec.

There have been quite a few radar observations showing thunderstorm tops extending about 5,000 feet into the stratosphere. Very severe thunderstorms with summits as much as 15,000 feet into the stratosphere have been reported. If these observations are reliable, it would mean that the storms contain updrafts of about 300 ft/sec (about 205 mph). These would truly be fantastic updrafts. Some scientists have questioned the correctness of the height measurements in these extreme cases. However, radar observations of storms to altitudes 5,000 to 10,000 feet into the stratosphere are not rare. We can be fairly certain on the basis of radar observations that in the upper parts of some thunderstorms, in the mature stage, updrafts can exceed 150 ft/sec.

An exciting research program in 1962–1963 should give some more definite answers about conditions in the upper parts of large thunderstorms. Airplanes were flown through thunderstorms at altitudes up to 40,000 feet. It has been reported that vertical velocities exceeding 200 ft/sec were encountered at the top altitude.

More will be said about new research projects in a later chapter. At this time, we can note that these extreme draft speeds support the inferences that at the tops of thunderstorms the vertical rivers of air flow extremely fast.

In Figure 4, the storm is at about the middle of the mature stage. The upper part of the cloud has begun to spread out under the influence of the stable layer at the stratosphere. In some cases, a widespread anvil cloud forms (Plate III). The texture of the cloud begins to change because the upper part of the cloud is now composed almost entirely of ice crystals. Temperature near the cloud top may be as low as —60 to —70°F.

As the mature stage progresses, the downdraft spreads through the cloud. Rainfall at the ground can become intense. The raindrops may be 5 millimeters in diameter. Even in still air, they would fall at speeds of 9 m/sec (1,800 ft/min). But they would be approaching the ground much faster. They are in air descending at speeds that may exceed 2,400 ft/min.

The quantity of air transported toward the ground is quite large, perhaps half as much as is carried upward by the updrafts. When it hits the ground, it rushes outward in all directions. Sometimes this occurs with such violence as to cause considerable property damage. Occasionally, crops are flattened as the downdraft air blows outward with great force. Most often, in local storms, the outflowing air serves the beneficial effect of making a miserably hot day bearable.

The coolest downdraft air comes from high up in the cloud. It has managed to descend to the earth because evaporative cooling made it heavy enough to fall all the way.

From the pilot's viewpoint, the mature stage of the thunderstorm is the worst. In passing through the cloud, the airplane is likely to undergo both positive and negative altitude changes. He might find the airplane falling at 1,000 feet and then suddenly being carried upward 2,000 feet. All along the route, there may be severe turbulence. Lightning is most frequent and active during the mature stage. Hail is likely to be encountered.

A thunderstorm is always to be avoided if possible, but by all means stay out of mature ones. Happily for the air traveler of today, modern commercial aircraft are equipped with radar sets for just that purpose.

As the downdraft spreads through the cloud and the updraft region gets smaller and smaller, the energy available to drive the thunderstorm is cut off. The mature stage, which may last for a period of 15 to 30 minutes, is drawing to a close. The thunderstorm moves into its final period, the "dissipating stage."

The dissipating stage

It is not easy to say exactly when the dissipating stage really begins. It's similar to trying to say when a man starts getting "old." When he is 80, he is clearly old, but at 50, he is merely on the way. A thunderstorm is headed for dissipation when more than half of it is composed of downdrafts. At this point, it may still have one or two strong gusts capable of shaking up an airplane. But for the most part, the cloud's activity is slowing down (see Figure 5).

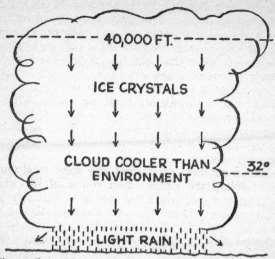

Figure 5. *The dissipating stage of a thunderstorm. The cloud is rapidly decaying. Downdrafts predominate and are weak. Turbulence and rainfall are diminishing.*

The downdraft speeds gradually diminish. Soon, only weak turbulence remains. The intensity of rain decreases. After all the large drops have fallen out of the cloud, only small quantities of rain will fall. Sometimes it comes down in the form of a light drizzle. As the cloud approaches the end of the line, its structure undergoes marked changes. It becomes grayish in appearance and begins to break up into layers. The part above the melting level will be composed almost entirely of crystals, while the lower part will be made of water droplets. With the passage of a few tens of minutes, the cloud begins to evaporate from all sides. Soon it will all be gone from sight as the droplets evaporate and the remaining parts blow away.

A long-lived storm

The life history we have just described is that of a single-cell local thunderstorm. Typically it will have a diameter of several miles. From inception to dissipation it might last an hour or less. Short-lived thunderstorms of this type are not unusual. Often, however, thunderstorms last longer. When they do, it is because the storm is composed of more than one cell. Before the first one completely dissipates, a new cell begins to form. In some cases, several of them, each in a different stage of development, can be in progress at the same time. Without special observation equipment, it is usually difficult to separate one cell from the next. As a result, visual observations give the impression of a single thunderstorm lasting many hours.

It still has not been determined why some local thunderstorms follow the simple, short course of life while others propagate themselves and remain in existence for extended periods. There is some evidence that it is somehow tied up with the wind distribution as well as with the moisture and stability of the atmosphere, but the relationship is not clear.

In the organized lines and groups of thunderstorms that produce violent weather, the wind plays a very important role. The next chapter deals with these severe storms.

4

SQUALL LINES AND
SEVERE THUNDERSTORMS

Most of the time, the coming of thunderstorms is viewed with pleasure rather than alarm. In many parts of the world, the rain they bring is vital to crops and municipal water supplies. Since thunderstorms usually occur during hot weather, the cool air they transport down from high in the sky is most welcome.

Sometimes, though, thunderstorms are treacherous guests. Instead of delivering a bountiful supply of raindrops, they hurl fusillades of ice balls. Hailstones 3 inches across can bombard the countryside, leaving the crops in ruin and the farmers in despair. The wheat in Kansas, the grapes in the Caucasus, and the fruit in Italy are often trampled under a hail of ice.

In the records of the Weather Bureau, you find reports such as this:

Lanham, Texas, April 30, 1958: Greatest damage at Lanham where crop loss was 100 percent. Solid hailstones 3 inches in diameter, some 5 inches. . . . 2 inches of rain in 20 minutes fell with hail. Hail reported between 2 and 3 feet deep.

How much energy would you imagine is released in a severe thunderstorm? The one that hit Lanham, was powerful. The quantity of energy released in the formation of the cloud was greater than the energy of 200 atomic bombs of the kind that wiped out Nagasaki.

Large hailstones are bad enough, but severe thunderstorms can roll out an even more powerful weapon. When a thunderstorm really wants to tear up the real estate, it produces a tornado. This vicious funnel of whirlwinds can perform destructive feats that sometimes defy belief. The damage to property is tremendous, but far worse is the fact that the tornado is a killer. When it comes, the sure place to be is underground. (See Plates IV and V.)

Devastating hail and tornadoes are the two features that clearly distinguish a severe storm from an ordinary one. Although meteorologists still are not sure about the essential differences between the two classes, they are getting closer to the answers. In recent years, severe storms have been getting a lot of attention. The vital questions are many: Under what conditions do these storms form? How do they differ in structure and life history from ordinary storms? Can you predict them? Is there any hope of developing means to control them? Before considering the properties of organized storms, let us first trace the development of severe-storm forecasting in the U.S.

The U. S. Weather Bureau did not issue forecasts of very severe thunderstorms until 1952. During the 1930's and the 1940's, it was recognized that little was known about conditions leading to the formation of large hailstones and particularly tornadoes. Also, it was believed that predictions of the formation of this type of weather would cause the public to panic. Some meteorologists did not share this view.

The first important steps toward changing the situation came from two officers in the Air Weather Service, the organization responsible for supplying weather information to the U. S. Air Force. Major E. J. Fawbush and Capt. R. C. Miller were stationed at Tinker Air Force Base, Oklahoma, a region where tornadoes strike with uncomfortable frequency. Starting about 1940, they had been studying conditions favorable for the formation of tornadoes. In addition to the distributions of temperature and moisture described earlier, they found that between the altitudes of 10,000 and 20,000 feet there usually was a jet of air with a speed in excess of 40 mph.

On March 20, 1948, violent tornadoes passed over Tinker Field and did more than $10,000,000 worth of destruction. Fifty airplanes were destroyed and 50 more were damaged. This event urged Major Fawbush and his associates to greater efforts. They were encouraged to develop specific procedures for tornado predictions. Starting in 1949, they began to make severe storm forecasts for Tinker Field and vicinity. As their skill and confidence increased, they enlarged their area of operations to cover most of the central United States.

Although the tornado forecasts by Major Fawbush's group were supposedly restricted to military installations, they began to leak out to the public. This inevitably led to a demand that severe weather forecasts be broadcast to everyone. So the Weather Bureau had to revise some policies. In 1942, the Bureau had set up networks of observers to report tornadoes. When one was located, warnings were issued to the public. Until one was actually spotted, however, no forecasts or warnings of tornadoes were broadcast. The pressure of public demand following the success of the Air Force caused the Weather Bureau to change its rules. It set up an organization to forecast severe storms for wide distribution via newspapers, radio, and television. The first forecast was issued in March, 1952.

The reaction to tornado and severe hail forecasts was not at all what had been feared. There was no panic or mad rush for the storm cellars. People accepted the forecasts as valuable pieces of information. Public education and experience has taught them that tornadoes are small and short-lived. A tornado forecast in western Oklahoma, for example, does not mean that the entire area will be covered with storms. Rather, it means that one or a few funnels will probably form. The forecast alerts everyone to be on the lookout for their occurrence. When one does form and is reported, the Weather Bureau issues detailed warnings to specific areas.

At the present time, forecasts of tornadoes and other violent weather are made by Weather Bureau forecasters in Kansas City, Mo., headed by Donald House. They have done an excellent job considering the present uncertainties about severe storms and the lack of adequate observations. The forecasts and warnings issued over the last 10 years have saved many lives. House would be the first to say that there is much room for improvement.

Lines of thunderstorms

Why do thunderstorms sometimes line up over a distance of many tens or hundreds of miles while at other times they scatter in a more or less random fashion?

There seem to be at least two possible reasons. We have already noted that in order for thunderstorms to develop at all, the air must be unstable and moist. At times, the pattern of atmospheric winds is such as to cause unstable, moist air to be concentrated along a fairly narrow corridor. Heating of the ground by the sun can lead to the formation of convective clouds along the particular zone where the right air mass conditions prevail. This could lead to the initiation of a line of thunderstorms, or "squall line," as it is often called. (See Plate VI.)

Sometimes moist, unstable air is present over a large area, but the thunderstorms suddenly begin to develop along a single line. When this happens, you can infer that the initiation was by a so-called "atmospheric disturbance." Something has passed through the regions and caused the lifting of the air along the line. The ascending air leads to the formation of convective clouds and thunderstorms. Various types of disturbances could bring this about. A common one is the "cold front."

When a large mass of cold air from the north begins to move southward, it pushes aside the warmer air in its way. The cold air forms a wedge that undercuts the warm air and forces it to rise (see Figure 6). Since the cold air is heavier than the warm air and is quite stable, there is little mixing between the 2 air masses. Because of the temperature differences on the 2 sides, the boundary can easily be followed on weather maps. It was given the name "front" by scientists who studied these phenomena during World War I. They compared it to the "fronts" separating opposing armies.

The rising warm air, if sufficiently moist and unstable,

53

may lead to the formation of thunderstorms along the front.

Sometimes disturbances in the wind field lead to a vertical displacement of air along a particular zone even

Figure 6.   *Schematic drawing of a cold front. As the cold air advances, warm, moist air is forced to rise; convective clouds and thunderstorms can be formed just ahead of the front.*

though a front does not exist. This situation comes about when the winds near the ground converge toward the zone. Since the ground blocks downward motions, the air rises. The forced ascent has the same effect as lifting along a cold front.

Once a line of thunderstorms has formed, it can propagate itself. The mechanism by which this is done will be discussed a little later. First, let us consider, in a little more detail, the atmospheric conditions on days when squall lines and severe thunderstorms are most likely to occur.

Ripe conditions for severe thunderstorms

About 20 years ago, 2 Weather Bureau meteorologists, Albert K. Showalter and Joe R. Fulks, made careful studies of the atmospheric conditions most favorable for the formation of severe thunderstorms. One of the first things they found was that very often there was a layer of very moist air near the surface with a deep, dry layer aloft. The boundary between the two was very sharp.

The variation of temperature with altitude also was quite distinct (it is shown in Figure 7). As you can see, in the lower moist layer, the temperature decreases with altitude up to the level marked B. Above the level

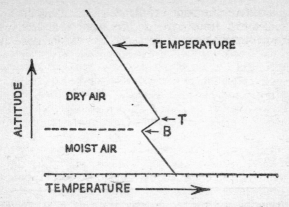

Figure 7. *Variation of temperature with height on day when severe thunderstorms are likely to form. A lower, moist body of air is separated from a deep region of dry air by a layer when the temperature increases with height. This layer is called a "temperature inversion."*

marked T, the expected lapse of temperature with altitude also prevails. Between B and T, however, the temperature increases rapidly. This layer is called a "temperature inversion" because the lapse rate is "inverted" from what is normally expected.

The inversion represents a very stable layer. It forms a lid on top of the moist region near the ground. As long as the inversion is strong, thermals formed by heating of the earth's surface cannot penetrate it. As a result, the moist layer gets warmer. It also becomes more humid as water vapor is added by evaporation from the ground and by the inflow of moist air trapped under the inversion.

Over the central United States, the temperature and moisture conditions represented in the illustration are accompanied by south winds near the ground and west winds aloft. The flow from the south brings moist air from the Gulf of Mexico over the country. At the higher altitudes, the winds from the dry regions over the Rocky Mountains sweep eastward.

In cases when severe thunderstorms form, the two

streams of air are not broad currents moving leisurely on their way. Instead, the flow is concentrated in fairly narrow, strong bands. These winds play an important part in the history of squall lines and severe thunderstorms. They not only help to set up the conditions for the initiation of the storms, they also vitally affect the maintenance and spread of the storms.

When we were discussing the formation of *local* thunderstorms, we noted that the atmosphere should be moist and unstable to fairly high altitudes. The conditions illustrated in Figure 7 clearly fail to satisfy these requirements. The inversion, which may vary in altitude from perhaps 5,000 to 8,000 feet above the ground, presents a stable barrier to the penetration of convection. Even if the inversion were weak, the very dry air aloft acts to destroy a cloud by evaporation. Furthermore, the diverging jets of air at high and low levels might be expected to tear apart any developing clouds. For these reasons you would suspect that a thunderstorm could not develop in the atmosphere represented by Figure 7. Your suspicions are partly correct. This atmosphere, if it remained unchanged, would not allow a thunderstorm to form. The reason why thunderstorms, and severe ones at that, do develop in these circumstances is that if the atmosphere pictured in Figure 7 is lifted, an explosive type of instability can be developed. When a cold front or some other type of disturbance causes the air to rise, the inversion may soon be destroyed. A lift of 3,000 to 5,000 feet is enough. In the case of a fast-moving cold front, this could take place in less than half an hour.

The inversion is destroyed because its top cools off faster than its bottom as long as they are lifted together. The moist air near the bottom becomes saturated with water vapor very quickly, and as it continues to rise, it cools at the moist-adiabatic rate (about $3.3°F.$ per 1,000 feet). On the other hand, the very dry top cools off at the dry-adiabatic rate (about $5.5°F$ per 1,000 feet). A continuation of these cooling rates leads to a very unstable atmosphere.

The lifting also spreads the moisture to higher levels

of the atmosphere. As a result, when clouds form, the outside air they entrain has a high humidity. The amount of evaporative cooling is small. A buoyant column of air is not hindered from continuing its growth to very great altitudes.

The sequence of events we have just described has been verified to a certain extent. The conditions of temperature and moisture shown in Figure 7 have been shown by meteorologists to be commonly observed on mornings of days when severe thunderstorms occur. However, in the vicinity of tornado-producing thunderstorms, the inversion is usually not found. Robert G. Beebe of the Weather Bureau * examined the properties of the atmosphere close, in time and space, to tornadic storms and reported that the inversions were not present and that the moisture extended to high levels.

It should be pointed out that although the ripe conditions of Figure 7 are common on days of severe weather, they do not always occur. Sometimes, especially near the coast of the Gulf of Mexico, violent thunderstorms occur when the air mass is unstable and moist through a deep layer. Occasionally, severe storms occur with very unstable air and low humidities near the ground. It is not clear why the same types of storms can form in atmospheres that appear to differ substantially. However, because of the fact that weather observations are taken many hours apart, it is difficult to know exactly how great differences really are. If more frequent temperature and humidity soundings of the free atmosphere were taken at more closely spaced stations, perhaps it would be found that the differences are smaller than they appear to be. Unfortunately, the equipment employed for tracking and recording the balloon-borne instruments is fairly expensive to procure and operate. As a result, the stations presently are located 200 to 300 miles apart and take observations at 12-hour intervals. This program does not yield adequate information either for research on, or the forecasting of, severe thunderstorms.

* Beebe is now president of Midwest Weather Service in Kansas City, Mo.

One of the chief differences between local thunderstorms and the organized ones is duration. Isolated thunderstorms may last for an hour or two. On the other hand, squall lines may persist for many hours, sometimes for more than a day. It is important to try to find out the reason for the differences.

Let us consider for a moment the movement of thunderstorms. If you could follow an individual thunderstorm cell, you would find that it tends to move with the wind at about 10,000 feet. Meteorologists sometimes call this the "steering level." The storm direction usually is slightly to the right of the wind and the speed is somewhat slower, but in general, the correlation between wind and cell velocities is good. Investigators on the Thunderstorm Project, and others, have shown this to be the case. However, they also demonstrated another very important fact. If, instead of following individual thunderstorm cells, you followed groups of thunderstorms, the center of the group could deviate from the 10,000-feet winds by a considerable margin. The reason for this disparity was easily tracked down.

As we noted earlier, a large thunderstorm is made up of many cells. As one dissipates, others develop. As a matter of fact, an existing one can effectively trigger the development of one or more new cells. They, in turn, can initiate others. The storm thus propagates itself. There is a tendency for new cells to be ahead of the existing storms, but sometimes they appear on the side or even to the rear. For this reason, if you were to follow the center of a region of thunderstorms, it could deviate considerably from the winds at the steering level.

One of the early ideas on the mechanism for the propagation of thunderstorms was advanced in 1941 by Henry T. Harrison and W. K. Orendorff, two United Air Lines meteorologists. They proposed that the cool air brought to the ground by the downdraft is an important factor in the spread of thunderstorms. If a line of thunderstorms was initially established along a front, the downdrafts could lead to a large pool of cool air spreading across the ground. As sketched in Figure 8, the

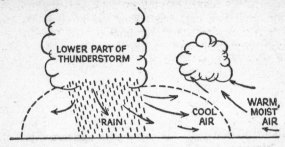

Figure 8. *Cool air rushing out from a thunderstorm produces a "miniature cold front." It causes the lifting of warm, moist air and the formation of new clouds.*

leading edge of the cool air acts somewhat like the cold front illustrated in Figure 6. Harrison and Orendorff referred to the boundary as a "miniature cold front." As it pushes ahead, it forces warm, moist air to rise. This process could lead to the release of the instability of the warm, moist air and the formation of new thunderstorms. The cool air often moves faster than the major cold front. As a result, the line of thunderstorms may move out to substantial distances ahead of the front.

In recent years, Tetsuya Fujita of the University of Chicago has studied the effects of spreading cool air in great detail. He has clearly shown that new thunderstorms are formed at the boundary. His meticulous studies show that as more thunderstorms form and feed the dome of cool air, it expands and leads to progressively longer lines of thunderstorms. The process continues until the cool air pushes into regions where the atmosphere is no longer moist and unstable.

The explanation for the propagation of thunderstorms based on the effects of spreading downdraft air adequately accounts for the propagation of many thunderstorm lines. In certain situations, particularly where the wind variations with height are small, it seems to be the most realistic explanation. However, it does not take into account the low- and high-level wind maxima that

59

are usually found when severe thunderstorms occur.

We should note that another theory for the propagation of squall lines was advanced by Morris Tepper of the Weather Bureau.* He theorized that if a cold front moved into a region where atmospheric conditions were like the ones illustrated in Figure 7, it could produce a wave on the inversion surface. The front could accomplish this by suddenly accelerating and then slow-

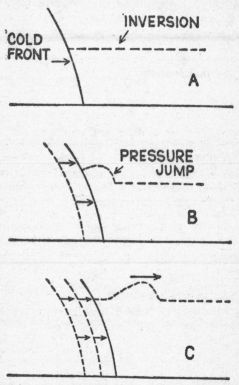

Figure 9. *The formation of a pressure jump on an inversion. If the cold front accelerates as shown (B), a wave forms on the inversion. If the front then slows down (C), the wave propagates ahead of the front.*

* Tepper is now affiliated with the National Aeronautics and Space Administration.

ing down (see Figure 9). Hydraulics engineers have shown that a wave, or "jump," such as the one shown can be produced on the top of a layer of water by giving it a sudden push with a piston. Once a jump is produced on the inversion, it propagates along the stable layer. Its speed depends on the height of the inversion and the temperatures above and below the inversion. Tepper suggested that as the jump moves along, it lifts the air and sets off thunderstorms. The evidence that lines of thunderstorms are propagated in this way is not strong, and this so-called "pressure jump theory" does not have many supporters.

Winds and thunderstorms

One of the puzzling aspects of the severe storm forecasting procedure was the requirement for a strong ribbon of winds at about 15,000 feet. The air usually blows from the west or southwest. At first, this seemed to be in conflict with many cloud observations. It is frequently seen that the tops of large convective clouds are torn away by strong winds aloft. Such observations, it was felt, meant that strong winds at higher altitudes would inhibit the growth of large, long-lived thunderstorms capable of producing violent weather. We now know that this is not always true. In situations where convection is weak and updrafts slow, strong winds aloft can shear the cloud tops and prevent further growth.

On the other hand, the results of the severe storm forecasting groups clearly show that severe thunderstorms, and line squalls as well, do develop when there are upper-level jets. Further work has led to the conclusion that not only can storms form with high wind speeds aloft, but indeed, the strong winds are necessary for the formation, maintenance, and spread of the thunderstorms.

Let us consider a large thunderstorm growing in an atmosphere in which the wind is from the west and increases with altitude. When the wind speed increases rapidly with height, we say that the "vertical wind shear" is strong. As the updraft extends to higher altitudes, it draws in air from outside the cloud. The air entrained

61

into the cloud at 15,000 feet, for example, has the horizontal velocity of the air outside the cloud at that altitude. Once inside the cloud, it mixes with air moving up from lower altitudes, where the wind speed was low. After the air from low altitudes mixes with that at 15,000 feet, the resultant velocity of the cloud air at that altitude is less than that of the air outside the cloud. The same mechanism holds true at higher levels of the cloud.

As a result of the mixing process, the cloud moves at a lower velocity than the upper level wind speeds. In 1948, Chester W. Newton, on the Thunderstorm Project, and Joanne Starr Malkus, at the University of Chicago, both developed equations describing this mechanism.

When a downdraft has formed, it carries downward air which is moving horizontally at a higher speed than the air outside the cloud at lower altitudes. As was the case in the updraft, there is mixing with outside air drawn into the cloud. The result of this process is that at low levels the cloud moves faster than the outside air.

In a large thunderstorm composed of many cells, the patterns of wind inside and outside is similar to the one illustrated in Figure 10.

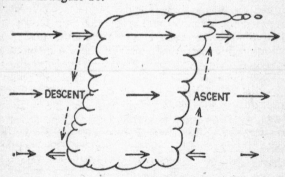

Figure 10.   *The air motions in and around a large thunderstorm system. In the clear air, the winds are from the west and increase steadily with height. The air movement inside the cloud shown by the solid arrows is different from that outside the cloud. At low levels the cloud moves faster than the wind; at upper levels it moves slower. The short double arrows show how the air outside the cloud moves relative to the cloud.*

Studies made by the Thunderstorm Project demonstrated that thunderstorms, as viewed with radar, tilted with altitude at a smaller rate than they would have if the clouds followed the wind exactly. It was found that the rate of tilt, or "cloud shear," as it is properly called, was about 50 to 75 percent of the vertical wind shear. This result conforms to the behavior one would expect with the wind pattern shown in Figure 10.

Clearly, if the air behind the cloud is moving faster than the cloud, the air must either be blowing through the cloud or around it. The latest studies indicate that both occur, but it appears that most of the air actually moves through the cloud.

The double arrows shown on the illustration in Figure 10 represent the airflow relative to the cloud. This means that if the cloud could suddenly be brought to rest, the air would be moving as shown by the double arrows. For example, near the cloud base on the front side, the cloud moves faster than the outside air. As a result, the cloud overtakes outside air. Relative to the cloud, the air is moving toward the cloud.

Chester W. Newton, who is now with the National Center for Atmospheric Research, Boulder, Colorado, has proposed that relative motions of the type shown in the illustration play a major part in the propagation of large thunderstorms and squall lines. The airflow pictured leads to convergence of air near the cloud base on the front side of the storm. As a result, the air near the ground is forced to rise. At the same time, there is divergence of the air along the front edge of the cloud at upper levels. This situation encourages the ascent of environment air along the leading edge of the storms. When moist, unstable air is present, the updraft initiated by relative motions of cloud and clear air can lead to the development of new thunderstorms.

To the rear of the large thunderstorm, the relative air motions are such as to cause divergence at low levels and convergence aloft. This situation leads to descent of outside air and the inhibition of new thunderstorms.

Newton's theory has been supported by extensive research conducted with the assistance of his wife, Harriet, a skilled meteorologist in her own right. They have built a strong case for the view that squall lines may propagate for long distances, roughly in the manner just described. In detail, their theory is considerably more elaborate than we have just described. For example, the Newtons have considered the more realistic case with south winds at low levels and west winds aloft. They have shown that this results in propagation of the storms somewhat to the right of the west winds. In essence, Newton's theory is based on the relative motions brought about by mixing of draft air and clear air. The process of new cloud formation at the forward edge of a line or group of thunderstorms is repeated many times. In this manner, a squall line moves forward until it reaches regions where the environment air is no longer moist and unstable.

The role of strong wind shear in the development of severe thunderstorms, and particularly hailstorms, has received a great deal of attention recently from Frank H. Ludlam, a prominent English meteorologist.

In 1960, Ludlam proposed that severe thunderstorms differ from ordinary thunderstorms in several important ways. He visualizes that in hail-producing storms, the updraft lasts for a long time, possibly an hour or more. In order for such a prolonged updraft to exist, it is essential that there be a strong vertical wind shear. Ludlam's model of a violent storm starts with a wind distribution similar to that pictured by Newton. As noted in Figure 10, the motion of air relative to the cloud is into the cloud at the front bottom and rear top and outward at the front top and rear bottom. Ludlam has suggested that in such a circumstance the air motion in and around the storm would be as shown in Figure 11. A model similar to this one had been suggested earlier by Joe R. Fulks of the Weather Bureau, but it was not published until 1962. One of the most important features of this model is that the updraft is tilted.

As the thunderstorm moves toward the east under the influence of west winds, air is fed into the updraft region at low levels and transported outward and aloft at the front.

Various arguments have been offered to support the

64

I: Cumulus clouds, 01:27 PM, August 17, 1962.

II: Cumulus congestus clouds, 01:37 PM, August 17, 1962.

III: Cumulonimbus cloud with anvil, 01:47 PM, August 17, 1962.

IV: A severe thunderstorm photographed from an altitude of 20,000 ft. Strong winds between 40 and 45,000 ft. lead to the growth of a pronounced anvil cloud. This thunderstorm produced a tornado.

V: A tornado funnel racing across country.

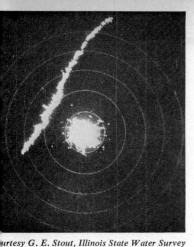

VI. A line of thunderstorms on a radar scope. The line is about 160 miles long and 5 to 10 miles wide.

VII Vertical cross section of a thunderstorm on a radar-scope. This storm was 5 mi. wide and reached a height of 40,000 ft.

VIII. Cross section of a hailstone about 1.4 inches in diameter. The small light-and-dark areas are small crystals and milky ice. The large, nearly uniform areas are large crystals and clear ice.

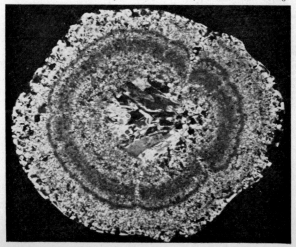

Courtesy L. E. Salanave

IX: A forked lightning flash over Arizona.

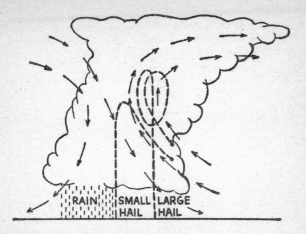

Figure 11. *Frank H. Ludlam's model of a severe thunderstorm producing large hail. The thin, solid lines show air movement relative to the cloud. The heavy, broken lines show the trajectories of growing hailstones.*

idea that this process can continue for a fairly long time. A detailed study of a hail-producing thunderstorm by means of radar showed that its shape and size varied very little over a period of about 30 minutes. It had been observed that the anvil tops of some hail-producing thunderstorms sometimes extend many tens of miles downwind. This result indicates a more or less continuous stream of air out of the top of the cloud on its forward edge.

Another important observational fact supporting Ludlam's theory is supplied by hail reports. On many occasions, hailstorms produce a long, narrow band of hail perhaps 20 miles long. Sometimes the trail of hail is much longer. It is argued that this is caused by a large, long-lived thunderstorm moving with the wind at the so-called steering level.

A strong point in favor of Ludlam's theory is that his thunderstorm model appears to satisfy the requirements for producing large hailstones. Calculations have indicated that in order for stones to grow several inches in diameter, it is necessary that they remain inside the cloud for periods of tens of minutes. Furthermore, they should be supported by the air in the supercooled regions of the cloud. At one time it was thought that in order to account for the layers of clear and opaque ice often observed in hailstones, it was necessary for the growing stones to oscillate above and below the melting level. It now is known that this is not the case. If the stone moves first through regions of the cloud with large quantities of supercooled cloud droplets and then through regions of small quantities, layers of clear and opaque ice can be formed.

Ludlam's model allows the growing stones to stay in the cloud a long time. As shown in Figure 11, the wind shear causes the updraft to tilt. Growing stones follow the path shown by the heavy broken lines. They are carried by the updraft to higher altitudes. When they reach regions where the updraft is weak, they may fall out of the cloud as small hail. In some cases, the stones fall back into the strong updraft core and repeat the cycle of being carried up to higher altitudes again. Very large stones (greater than 2 inches in diameter) may make several journeys up and down before they finally become so heavy that they fall right through the updraft. Clearly, in order to transport and support giant hailstones, very large updrafts are needed. Calculations show that the fall speed of a hailstone 2 inches in diameter is about 6,000 ft/min. The updrafts must exceed this speed.

Although Ludlam's theory still is under the scrutiny of many meteorologists, including Ludlam himself, it does appear to explain many known features of those thunderstorms producing large hail.

Before leaving the subject of the structure of severe thunderstorms, we should consider one more important point. In earlier sections, we noted that the major source of convective energy was heat released when moist, unstable air ascended in the updraft. It is important to realize that energy can also be released in the downdraft. In an unstable atmosphere, the air at higher levels is "potentially cold." When the air is cooled by evaporation, it becomes heavier than the surrounding air and begins to descend. As long as evaporation continues, descent continues. The energy released in this process is available for maintaining the motions in the cloud. The cloud models discussed in this section call for the introduction into the thunderstorm of potentially cold air at high levels. This can take place effectively when there is strong wind shear. Thus the presence of wind shear makes it possible for thunderstorms better to tap the energy latent in the low-level, moist, warm air, as well as the high-level, dry, cool air.

In summary, then, the conditions that favor the formation of violent storms may be described as follows: Before the clouds begin forming, a layer of very moist air is surmounted by a deep layer of dry air. The two layers are separated by a shallow inversion, a layer in which the temperature increases with height. Lifting of the entire column of air leads to a very unstable air mass and the initiation of convective clouds and thunderstorms. Strong vertical wind shear, particularly with a jet of westerly winds aloft, makes it possible for the storms to have long durations and propagate over long distances. Because of the high instabilities and wind shear, strong tilted updrafts can develop. In this situation, large hailstones can be grown. Also, for reasons not clearly understood, conditions favorable for the formation of large hail also appear to be favorable for the development of tornadoes.

5

THUNDERSTORM WEATHER
NEAR THE GROUND

We have already looked at a thunderstorm through the eyes of a pilot. The view is not a pleasing one. Not too many years ago it was terrifying. When boiling masses of black clouds had to be penetrated, it was done with fingers crossed and a silent prayer. Modern technology has taken most of the claws out of the lion of the sky. First of all, airborne radar permits the pilot to locate thunderstorms far enough ahead so that he can take evasive action. When it is necessary to go through a squall line, the radar shows the pilot the smoothest path.

Another major step in reducing the hazards of thunderstorms has been the development of jet airplanes that can fly over the tops of most storms. By staying at altitudes of 35,000 to 40,000 feet, the airplanes can usually pass over or fly around them. When an airplane has to go through a line of thunderstorms extending to great heights, the radar guides the way.

The thunderstorms that still represent problems are those in the vicinity of the airports. As airplanes take off and land, they sometimes are forced to pass through some rough air. Airborne and ground-based radar makes these parts of the flights much less uncomfortable than they used to be.

Many of us fly often. We have seen the awesome

sight of a nighttime thunderstorm being brightly illuminated by flashes of lightning. The downward drop
of an airplane and the tug of the seat belt are familiar
experiences, though they are becoming less frequent.
Most people never have known, and probably will never
know, the sensation of feeling "the bottom drop out of
the sky." To them the thunderstorm is a mystery of a
different kind. The sudden transformation of a peaceful, sunny day into a wild scene of cascading rain and
hail, violent winds, crackling lightning, and rolling thunder is enough to prove that a thunderstorm is something
special.

Let us examine in some detail the weather conditions
at the ground during the passage of a thunderstorm. In
the next chapter, we shall consider some of the properties of lightning and thunder.

Thunderstorm rainfall

The thunderstorm is a good rain machine. It can
produce staggering quantities in short periods of time.
The reasons for this are not difficult to understand.

As we noted earlier, clouds begin to form when moist
air rises and is cooled until it reaches saturation. At this
time, condensation takes place on minute salt and other
particles in the air. As the updraft carries the air to
higher altitudes, more and more quantities of water
vapor become available for the growth of cloud droplets.
When large cloud droplets or ice crystals have formed,
they continue to grow rapidly by colliding with the
small droplets constantly being formed. As the thunderstorm penetrates to greater heights, the quantities of
water and ice particles become very large.

In a cloud with strong updrafts, the water and ice
particles cannot fall to the ground. Even large hailstones
are suspended or carried upward. As a result, a thunderstorm becomes a storehouse of precipitation. When
the amount of ice and water in storage becomes too
large, the buoyancy of the updraft can be overcome.
A downdraft is started. The precipitation then falls to the
ground.

The speed at which a raindrop approaches the ground depends not only on its size, but also on the strength of the downdraft. A raindrop 0.2 inch in diameter falls at about 1,800 ft/min in *still air*. In a downdraft of 2,000 ft/min, such a drop will approach the ground at a speed of 3,800 ft/min—that is, the sum of 1,800 and 2,000 ft/min. If there are many large drops in a very strong downdraft, the rate of rainfall can be very high.

Some rainfall records illustrate this point. The table below was prepared from data published by the U. S. Weather Bureau. It shows the greatest quantities measured for various time periods in various parts of the world. Some of these figures are not regarded as being completely documented, but there are no positive grounds for rejecting them.

Time Period	Location	Date	Quantity of rain in inches
1 min	Opid's Camp, Calif.	April 5, 1926	0.65
5 min	Porto Bello, Panama	Nov. 29, 1911	2.5
15 min	Plumb Point, Jamaica	May 12, 1916	8
1 hour	Catskill, N. Y.	July 26, 1819	10

Clearly, on some occasions truly fantastic rainfall rates occur. Consider the devastation that can occur in a rain such as the one that fell on Plumb Point, Jamaica— 8 inches in just 15 minutes. This rain probably fell from a large thunderstorm. When several thunderstorms occur in rapid succession, the total amount over a period of many hours is nearly unbelievable. For example, at Baguio, Philippine Islands, on July 14 and 15, 1911, the staggering total of 46 inches of rain fell during a 24-hour period. An almost continuous series of severe thunderstorms continued to dump huge quantities for an entire day.

Fortunately, the types of storms producing the extreme rainfalls just cited are not common. If they were, those regions of the world that now are the richest agriculturally would be worth little. For example, the central part of the United States, which produces tremendous quantities of corn, beans, and grains, depends on thunderstorm rainfall during the growing season. However, the precipitation is expected to come regularly and in moderate quantities. An average of perhaps an inch per week during July and August would be quite satisfactory. It almost never occurs this regularly, but the normal rainfall for the summer gives almost an equivalent amount of rain. For example, the average rainfall for June, July and August in St. Louis, Missouri, is 10.5 inches, an average of about 0.8 inch per week. During those infrequent years when torrential storms occur, the damage in the form of flooded fields and crushed plants runs into the millions of dollars.

The rainfall from a typical thunderstorm over the United States reaches its maximum rate within several minutes after the first drops reach the ground. The rate remains high for a period of 5 to 15 minutes and then gradually diminishes. On the average, the rain from a single storm lasts 20 to 30 minutes. Of course, when there are many thunderstorms passing over a station, there may be several bursts of heavy rain with intermediate periods of light rain.

The largest amounts of rain occur when organized lines of thunderstorms form and move in such a way that several mature thunderstorms pass over the same location. In such instances, record rainfalls and floods are the result.

We have already noted that heavy rainfall occurs when there are large quantities of water and ice particles and strong downdrafts. The latter is the cause of another familiar feature of the thunderstorm—the outrush of cool air just before the rain.

Gusty winds before the storm

As a thunderstorm goes through its life cycle, the wind field under the cloud undergoes some important changes. During the early part of storm growth, the surface winds converge toward the cloud. The amount of convergence is small and usually cannot be detected

71

except by the use of sensitive instruments. Measurements show that winds over a radius of 6 to 8 miles from active convective clouds are deviated so as to feed air into the cloud base. When the winds before the storm are light, the effects of convergence may be such as to cause them to fall almost to a dead calm. The air becomes still; the humidity makes it uncomfortable. The stage is set for a dramatic change.

The downdraft performs the sudden transformation. When the mass of cool, descending air strikes the ground, it rushes out in all directions. Mostly it goes in the direction of the winds at the upper levels. Over the United States, this means that usually the strongest push of cool, gusty air is toward the east and northeast.

When the downdraft persists, a rapidly enlarging dome of cool air is produced (see Figure 8). Its boundaries are narrow zones with transitions between the warm, unstable air surrounding the cloud and the cool, stable air brought down from high in the cloud. In Chapter 4, we mentioned that the forward edge of the boundary has been called a miniature cold front because it separates regions of air having distinctly different properties. As it spreads horizontally, it causes the warm air to rise and leads to the formation of new convective clouds and thunderstorms.

Ever since the first wind-speed measuring device, an anemometer, was set up, measurements of the wind gusts at the leading edge of the so-called cold dome have been accumulating. Most of the time, the gusts are below about 30 mph, but often they are stronger than 40 mph. Sometimes they are very much stronger—occasionally they exceed hurricane-force winds of 75 mph. When this occurs, there is a great amount of damage to property. Roofs may be stripped, power and telephone lines blown down. Television antennas mounted on housetops are ready victims of the powerful winds. Crops—wheat, corn, soybeans, etc.—can be badly mangled. As a matter of fact, in some parts of the United States, the strong, straight winds blowing out of a thunderstorm are called "plow

72

winds." Clearly, this term is a recognition of the complete devastation the wind can cause.

Until about 15 years ago, most observations of the cold dome were made with one or just a few instruments. The devices were mounted in some convenient place and awaited the passage of a thunderstorm. Of course, the weather services of the world have had many anemometers as well as temperature, pressure, and humidity devices for many decades. However, most standard weather observing instruments are not well suited for studying the detailed properties of thunderstorm weather near the ground. The chief reason for this is that the instruments faithfully reproduce only those events that evolve slowly. Properly speaking, you would say that the response times of the sensing devices and the recorders are too slow. Since the weather services are primarily concerned with forecasting the weather 12, 24, or 48 hours in advance, it is usually quite adequate to have slow-responding instruments.

Temperature increases during the day seldom exceed 3 to 4°F per hour and are usually much smaller. The same slow rates of temperature change occur during nighttime cooling. On the other hand, when the first gust of cool air from a thunderstorm passes over a station, the temperature may fall 10°F in a few minutes. The wind speed can increase by 30 to 40 mph in a matter of minutes and then almost as quickly fall 20 to 30 mph. In order to obtain good descriptions of the properties of the cold dome and the warm air around it, fast-responding and -recording instruments are needed.

Some detailed measurements were collected and analyzed prior to 1945, particularly by the German scientist G. A. Suckstorff, but the first extensive series of observations were made by the Thunderstorm Project. One of the aims of the program was to examine the weather near the ground in three dimensions as well as the variations with time. This could not be done with just a few stations. A network was needed.

During the 1946 season in Florida, a grid of 55 stations spaced approximately one mile apart was established in an area roughly 5 by 15 miles. At each station there were special instruments for measuring and recording wind, temperature, pressure, relative humidity, and rainfall. The following year, in Ohio, the network was changed somewhat. In order to cover a larger area, the 55 stations were spaced about 2 miles apart in a region 10 by 20 miles. When a thunderstorm reached maturity over the network and dropped its rain and cool air, it was possible to map the surface weather in detail.

The network also included equipment for making vertical soundings of temperature, pressure, and relative humidity. Balloon-borne instruments measured the values of these important quantities up to altitudes of over 50,000 feet. Finally, the growth of the clouds could be followed by means of radar and the airplane measurements discussed in Chapter 1.

Comprehensive analyses of the weather observations made at the ground were carried out by Harry Moses, one of the principal analysts of the Thunderstorm Project. The data collected by the dense network of stations also have been studied in detail by other scientists. Notable among them were Tepper and Williams of the Weather Bureau and Fujita and his colleagues at the University of Chicago. Each of these individuals has helped to build a reasonable picture of the cold dome and how it behaves.

Although in more recent years other networks of stations have been installed and operated, the data collected by the Thunderstorm Project is still being studied. This fact may seem surprising because some 15 years have elapsed since it was gathered. However, it should be noted that the observations are of an unusually high quality. Also, the quantity of measurements is quite large. When 5 instruments operate night and day at 55 stations for 4 months, the records fill many file cabinets.

What has been learned from the analyses of these records and those collected over the last decade?

First of all, it is clear that the quantity of cool air in the dome is related to the quantity of rainfall. This result is indicative of the relationship between the rain and the downdraft. As long as there are precipitation particles evaporating, the descending air remains cooler and heavier than the air outside the cloud. In this situation, the air continues to pour down on the top of the spreading cold dome.

The layer of cool air is not very deep once it moves out from under the thunderstorm. The German scientist Harold Koschmieder attempted to learn more about this point by installing instruments on the Eiffel Tower. However, the Tower, extending to about 1,000 feet, was not high enough to reach the top of the cool air. Balloon measurements show that this top varies from perhaps 2,000 to 5,000 feet. Once the thunderstorm producing the cool air has dissipated and cut off the supply, the dome sinks and flattens out.

Although the sudden acceleration of wind accompanying the arrival of the cool air is quite pronounced at the surface, the wind velocities are strongest 500 to 1,000 feet above the ground. Surface friction accounts for this fact. As the cool air begins to run rapidly outward, the lowest air layers are slowed down because of rough terrain, trees, rocks, and so forth. The air above the ground does suffer these strong decelerating forces. It is true that as the lowest layer of air is retarded, it in turn acts to retard the layer of air above it. But this effect is relatively small. As a result, the maximum gust velocities occur above the ground. The rapid increase of wind speed with height can have important consequences in aviation.

When the wind changes rapidly over short distances, turbulent eddies are produced even when no clouds are present. We noted earlier that jet airplanes can fly over or around the tops of most thunderstorms. By so doing, they can successfully avoid severe turbulence produced by the convective clouds. This does not mean, however, that jet airplanes never encounter turbulence. On the contrary, jet pilots have found that high in the atmosphere, in perfectly clear weather, they often pass through regions of bumpy air. Clear air turbulence, or "CAT," as it is often called, usually is quite light, but occasionally an airplane gets a few good shakes. This is a far cry from the type of turbulence encountered in a full-blown thunderstorm, but it still is a problem. It is known that much of the CAT is caused by eddies produced in regions of strong wind shear.

The rapid changes of wind speed through the cold dome can have similar effects to those normally experienced in regions of high wind speeds at high altitudes. Fairly strong turbulence can be produced. Since this occurs close to the ground, it can be serious. An airplane in the hands of an inexperienced pilot can be thrown out of control at a time when control is of the utmost importance—at takeoff or landing. The lesson to be kept in mind is that if high gusty winds are sweeping across an airport, it is wise to allow them to subside before attempting to take off or land.

The great changes of wind velocity occur just behind the front edge of the cold dome. After about 20 minutes has elapsed from the time of the first gust of cool air, the edge will have moved often 5 miles or so. By this time the wind speed in the cool air will normally have dropped considerably. Of course, in some cases, the period of strong gusty winds can last several times 20 minutes, but these cases are exceptional ones.

When a local thunderstorm is the source, the dome of cool air may spread out over an area perhaps 10 miles in diameter. Mixing with outside air leads to its rapid destruction. As we know from common experiences, on some days thunderstorms provide little relief from the heat. The volumes of rain and cool air they produce are too small to overcome the overpowering effects of the sun and the large quantities of warm air.

On other days, the downdraft air can completely change the weather conditions over a region more than 100 miles wide. This is most likely to occur when there are organized lines and groups of thunderstorms. When many storms, at almost the same time, discharge huge quantities of cool air, they produce a cold dome that covers very large regions. The passage of the gusty front edge of the cold body of air can drop the temperature 10 to 15 degrees or more in perhaps 10 minutes and keep it there for hours.

Sometimes the effects of the thunderstorm downdraft may modify the wind, temperature, and pressure conditions over a region large enough to be detected by the weather stations more than 100 miles apart. The effects of the cool air are reflected in the wind pattern, but are usually more pronounced in the form of temperature and pressure changes. Let us examine these points in a little more detail.

Temperatures under a thunderstorm

As we all know, thunderstorms are most common in the summertime, when temperatures at the ground are high. We noted in Chapter 2 that the thunderstorm is one of nature's mechanisms for transporting heat upward. It should be recognized, before going on, that when the air is unstable—that is, when the temperature decreases rapidly with height—convective clouds and thunderstorms can form even though temperatures at the ground are fairly low. Occasionally thunderstorms occur in the winter, but these are rare and are caused by the lifting of unstable air by a front or other disturbance. Most thunderstorms form when the sun heats the ground and the lower layers of the atmosphere to temperatures above about 80°F.

Thunderstorms are most likely over areas that are warmer than the surroundings. For example, in hilly or mountainous regions, the first convective clouds and thunderstorms are most likely over the hills or mountains. Also, in a region where there are lakes, the clouds will form more often over dry land than over the lakes because the ground warms up much more rapidly than the water.

Over large, fairly uniform areas, the details of the surface have not been shown to be important. It has been proposed that the difference in temperature between a newly plowed field and a grassy one would be sufficient to favor cloud formation over the plowed one. Although this idea is a reasonable one, no one has convincingly shown it to be true. The Thunderstorm Project was unable to detect any differences in the temperature field under newly forming convective clouds.

Of course, once the downdraft begins, the changes of temperature are very pronounced. The cool air released during the mature stage leads to a rapid fall in the temperature. Figure 12 illustrates the variation of temperature and other weather factors as a thunderstorm passed

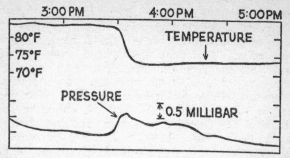

Figure 12. *Variation of temperature and pressure accompanying the passage of a thunderstorm over a station. Measurements by the Thunderstorm Project.*

a station. This example is fairly typical. It shows that the temperature dropped to its lowest point about 10 to 15 minutes after the arrival of the cool air.

When a thunderstorm cell matures over a network of closely spaced stations, its location is clearly shown in

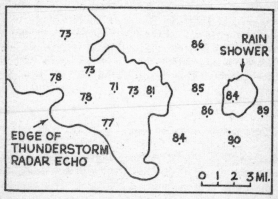

Figure 13. *The temperature pattern under a thunderstorm and a small shower. The temperature at selected stations of the Florida network of the Thunderstorm Project shows the cooling effect of the downdraft. Under the thunderstorm, temperatures are as low as 71°F. In the southeast corner of the network, only about 8 miles from the point where the temperature is 71°F, one station recorded 90°F.*

78

the temperature field. Figure 13 was taken from one of the reports of the Thunderstorm Project. It shows the pattern of temperatures over the Florida network. As we noted earlier, 55 stations were spaced about one mile apart. Two thunderstorm cells were producing down-drafts over the area at the same time. Their locations can be seen as regions of reduced temperature. The storm over the western end of the network was quite large and active. The downdraft was strong and cool. Temper-ature at the ground right under it fell to below 71°F. This represented a very pronounced cooling. As you can see, the stations in the southeast corner of the network were reporting temperatures of about 90°F. These were the general conditions before the storm occurred. Thus, this particular thunderstorm caused a temperature reduc-tion of at least 19°F.

The rain shower over the eastern end of the network was still young and small at the time of this map. Mini-mum temperatures were about 84°F. For the next 30 minutes the storm increased in size and the downdraft strengthened. As a result, the surface temperatures con-tinued to fall. The minimum was measured at 76°F.

The thunderstorms represented in the illustration oc-curred at 1:30 P.M. on July 9, 1946, over the town of St. Cloud, Florida. Surely they must have been welcomed by the residents. They turned a hot, humid day into a pleasant one.

Pressure variations under a storm

The term *pressure* is familiar to everyone. It is used in a variety of ways, but to a physicist it has one pre-cise meaning. It is defined as the force on a unit area. When we speak of atmospheric pressure, we mean just that—the force on a unit of area. The average atmos-pheric pressure at sea level is 14.7 pounds of force per square inch. If you have never thought about this point before, you might ask, "Where does the 14.7 pounds of force come from?" Quite simply, it is the weight of the air in the atmosphere in a column 1-inch square extend-ing from sea level to the top of the atmosphere.

We have cited the figure 14.7 lbs/in² because it is familiar to many people. There are other ways to express pressure. If you take a hollow tube about 30 inches long sealed at one end, fill it with mercury, then turn it upside down and put the open end in a dish of mercury, only a small quantity of fluid will flow out of the tube. On an average day, the height of the column of mercury will stand at 29.92 inches. The reason why the fluid remains in the tube is that the force of the atmosphere on the surface of the mercury in the dish pushes it up the tube. The length of the column of mercury is such that its total weight is just equal to the total weight of the atmosphere on the surface of the mercury outside the tube. This experiment was first performed in 1643 by Torricelli. The principle is still employed in modern mercury barometers. Pressure is measured by precisely reading the length of the mercury column. As you would suspect, there are various other schemes for measuring pressure besides this one.

Most reports of atmospheric pressure given over radio and television weather shows are in inches of mercury. Meteorologists have found it convenient to employ still a different measure of atmospheric pressure—the millibar. Standard atmospheric pressure in this system is 1013.2 millibars. This quantity comes from the centimeters-grams-seconds system of units.

For centuries, it has been recognized that atmospheric pressure is a good indicator of weather events. Of course, it is far from perfect and sometimes can be quite misleading, but, in general, when the pressure falls, bad weather is more likely than good weather. If you look at the weather maps published in many newspapers and shown on television shows, it is evident that areas of low pressure are regions with clouds and precipitation. A pronounced example of the fall in pressure accompanied by poor weather is found with hurricanes. In these violent storms, the pressure at the ground falls to very low values. In one tropical storm in the Philippine Islands, a pressure as low as 887 millibars (26.18 inches of mercury) was reported.

In the center of tornadoes, pressures may fall as low or possibly even lower than they do in hurricanes, but good measurements are very scarce. First of all, these storms are quite small—almost always less than a mile in diameter—and therefore seldom pass right over a station with a recording barometer. Secondly, tornadoes are so destructive that the most severe ones do not leave satisfactory recordings behind.

The pressure story under a thunderstorm is the reverse of that under a tornado or the much larger storm systems of tropical or higher latitudes. During the early stages of the growth of the convective clouds, the pressure does usually show a small decrease of less than 1 millibar. However, the most distinctive feature of the pressure pattern when a mature thunderstorm passes overhead is a rise in pressure rather than a fall.

In order to understand why the pressure increases, it is necessary to know what factors cause an increase in the weight of the atmosphere. We can assume that the depth of the atmosphere is constant. The weight increases as the weight per unit volume of air increases. When the air is cool and dry, it is heavier than when it is warm and moist.

During the cumulus stage of thunderstorm development, the air inside the cloud is warmer and more moist than that on the outside. As a result, a column of air passing through the cloud is lighter. The pressure under the cloud is reduced. The weight of the liquid droplets acts to increase the pressure, but the effect is not large enough to compensate for the effects of higher temperatures.

When the cloud reaches the mature stage with large quantities of precipitation and a strong downdraft, the situation changes drastically. The cool, downdraft air which we discussed earlier is heavier than the surrounding warm air and leads to an increase in pressure. The dome of cool air forming under and around the cloud is accompanied by a so-called "pressure dome." This term comes from the appearance of the curve on the chart of a barograph—a recording barometer. The curve rises rapidly and stays high for a period of 30 minutes to several hours, depending on the size of the region of cool air.

When a line of thunderstorms produces a large dome

of cool air that sweeps across the country, there may be almost simultaneous sharp increases of pressure at several stations. Rises as great as 6 millibars in 2 minutes have been recorded.

In the last chapter, we mentioned that Morris Tepper proposed that these lines of so-called "pressure jumps" were caused by waves in the atmosphere. He further theorized that the propagating waves initiated the thunderstorms.

Most scientists who have studied the pressure perturbations associated with thunderstorm lines do not subscribe to Tepper's theory. Instead, they believe that the thunderstorms themselves produce the pressure jumps. As already noted, the storms do this by discharging cool air, which is heavier than the warm, moist air in which the storms develop.

The Thunderstorm Project reported an interesting feature of the pressure dome. Stations directly under a mature thunderstorm sometimes show a sharp hump on top of the pressure dome. Since it occurs directly under an active thunderstorm, this so-called "pressure nose" is considered to be a result of the vertical motions in the downdraft. However, the exact mechanism is not understood.

At one time it was speculated that because the arrival of thunderstorms is associated with sudden pressure rises, it might be possible to devise storm-warning techniques based on this fact. Unfortunately, the elapsed time between the pressure jump and the thunderstorm is too small to make this idea a practical one. Radar sets can do the job much better. They can detect storms when they are many miles away and track them as they move.

Summary

The growth and dissipation of a thunderstorm is reflected in the weather at the surface. Even before any rain appears, small changes in the wind and pressure show the presence of a rising column of air. When the storm reaches maturity and rain pours down, very marked changes of wind, temperature, and pressure take place. They are indicative of a downdraft transporting cool air to the ground in large quantities. The surface weather changes clearly show that the thunderstorm is effectively mixing the atmosphere. It transports heat upward and acts to make the atmosphere more stable.

6

LIGHTNING AND THUNDER

A huge thunderstorm at full maturity is truly magnificent to behold. It extends upward like a huge corrugated pillar topped by a filmy cap of white. Rain, perhaps hail, pour out of its base, accompanied by large masses of gusty air, which stir up dust and leaves. Finally, and most obviously, there are the trademarks of this storm—lightning and thunder.

For thousands of years, people were terrorized and mystified by lightning. Sometimes it streaked out of the sky and set a tree or a dwelling aflame. Occasionally people and animals were instantly killed. It is no wonder that lightning was thought to be a weapon of the gods.

Socrates, Aristotle, and other Greek philosophers began to see the sky and the weather as part of nature. Another 2,000 years had to pass before some curious individuals set the stage for learning some indisputable facts about lightning.

In the late sixteenth century, scientists began to study the phenomenon we now call electricity. Knowledge of its properties began to accumulate at an ever-increasing pace. As early as 1708, an English scientist, William Wall, observed that sparks and noise produced when static electricity was discharged had some similarity to lightning and thunder. However, another 45 years came and went before convincing experiments were performed showing that lightning was an electrical discharge. These were, of course, those suggested and carried out by Benjamin Franklin. His most famous experiment was to fly a kite during a thunderstorm and demonstrate that the clouds were electrically charged. According to the Russian literature, similar experiments were in progress in Russia at about the same time, under the leadership of 2 famous scientists, Mikhail V. Lomonosov and Georgi W. Richmann. The latter was electrocuted in the course of one of the experiments when lightning came too close.

Some of Franklin's investigations and some of his conclusions about thunderstorm electricity are truly remarkable. More than 200 years have passed since he started his work. During that time, we have learned a great deal about lightning and thunder. We have not learned enough, however, and some fundamental questions still remain unanswered. There has been no shortage of ideas. As we shall see, many clever theories have been formulated. The chief difficulty has been to collect satisfactory measurements of the electrical properties of thunderclouds and the air surrounding them.

Electrical structure of a thunderstorm

For many years, there were serious uncertainties about the electrical structure of thunderstorms. This is no longer the case. Details of the distribution of electric charge still are not clear, but the overall picture is reasonably well known.

Before discussing the charge on clouds, let us first briefly note the techniques employed for its measurement. With suitable instruments it is possible to measure the electrical charge on individual drops or on large volumes of air or droplets. Unfortunately, observations of this kind are difficult to make inside a cloud. If airplanes are used to carry the equipment, they interfere with the measurements because they become charged themselves. Some success has been had by suspending equipment from balloons, although the experiments suffer because the balloons' position cannot be controlled very well. Some useful measurements with aircraft have been made, but because extreme care must be taken, the quantity has been small.

Most of our information about the charge on clouds has come from measuring the so-called "electric field." When two objects having different electric charges are separated, an electric field exists between them. The strength of the field depends on the magnitude of the charges and the distance between the objects. Many instruments have been developed for measuring the strength of an electric field. They have been used extensively on the ground and on airplanes.

In the atmosphere, there is virtually always an electric field. The earth is negatively charged relative to the upper atmosphere. During fair weather, the electric field is about 30 volts/foot and is designated as being negative in sign. This means that if you had a suitable voltage-reading instrument and took measurements at the surface of the earth and at an altitude of 3 feet, you would find the voltage at the higher altitude to be 90 volts greater than at the earth's surface.

When a cumulus cloud begins to form overhead, this is indicated by the change of the electrical field. The sign of the field reverses, showing that the cloud has become predominantly negative. Field strengths up to 150 volts/foot have been measured in the vicinity of such a cloud.

As the convective cloud continues to grow, the charging mechanism—or possibly mechanisms—continues to operate. It leads to a cloud with 2 major centers of charge. Just above the melting level (where the temperature is 32°F), a large region of negative charge is formed. The upper parts of the cloud—and possibly the edges of the cloud, too—becomes positively charged. We say the thunderstorm has a "dipole" charge—that is, there are two electrical poles, one negative and one positive.

When rain begins to fall from a thunderstorm, a second, smaller region of positive charge is sometimes formed in the lower part of the cloud. At this stage in the cloud's life, it is charged as shown schematically in Figure 14. In examining this illustration, you should realize that the electrical pattern is not quite as simple as

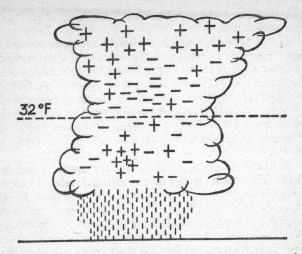

32°F

Figure 14. *The electrical charge of a fully developed thunderstorm. The small center of positive charge near the cloud base is associated with falling rain. The main negative region surmounted by a large positive one is common to virtually all thunderstorms, but the lower positive center is only sometimes present.*

shown here. For example, in the negative region, there are many positively charged cloud and precipitation particles. The region is designated as negative because the negative charges greatly outnumber the positive ones. Another important point is that the charges are not uniformly spread through the cloud. Instead, there are small pockets of charges within each of the major charge regions.

It is clear from seeing the consequences of lightning that the total quantity of electrical energy stored in a thundercloud just before a lightning stroke is quite substantial. Each of the two main charge regions may contain perhaps 20 coulombs, sometimes less, sometimes more. Now, a coulomb is not necessarily a large quantity of electric charge. If two parallel metal plates are charged with 20 coulombs but have a small voltage difference between them, little excitement will be caused

87

when the plates are discharged slowly. On the other hand, the electric potential between the centers of charge in a thundercloud and between the cloud and ground is very large; in some instances, it exceeds 100,000,000 volts. If, as occurs in a lightning flash, the centers are discharged in a few thousandths of a second, spectacular events occur. In that brief instant, tremendous electric currents may produce extremely high temperatures. More will be said about this subject in a later section.

As the electric charge stored in the growing convective cloud becomes larger and larger, the electric fields in and below the cloud become stronger and stronger. As we recall, in fair weather the electric field strength is about 30 volts/foot. Around cumulus clouds it is up to 150 volts/foot. In the thundercloud just before a lightning flash, the field should be about 300,000/ volts/foot. No actual observations have revealed fields this large, but we know that they must exist at the point where the electrical discharge begins. Laboratory investigations have shown that in order to get electric sparks or arcs through air containing raindrops, these extremely intense electric fields are needed.

Before going into a discussion of lightning, let us look at the possible mechanisms that may account for the production and separation of electric charges in a thundercloud.

Charging a thundercloud

Over the last 40 years, there have been many theories for the charging of thunderstorms. Some of them are inconsistent with the known facts and have since been rejected. At the present time, however, there are still four or five proposals that have some merit. By this we mean that each of the theories explains some of the facts. Unfortunately, the observational evidence accumulated over the years is not adequate to allow the rejection of all but one or two.

A completely satisfactory theory of thunderstorm electrification should explain all the accepted observational facts. In addition to the charge distribution discussed in the preceding section, the theory must also account for the proper rate of charging. In particular, it is necessary that the rate be large enough for the first lightning stroke to occur some 10 to 20 minutes after precipitation droplets have first appeared in the cloud.

A substantial number of the scientists studying this problem are convinced that rapid thunderstorm electrification does not take place until ice particles have been formed in the cloud. Over the continental regions of the earth outside the tropics, lightning is rare in clouds composed entirely of liquid drops. There is little doubt that ice particles are usually present when the first flash appears. However, this still does not settle the vital question of whether or not the ice particles are absolutely essential. It is possible that in a rapidly building convective cloud, the charging mechanism can be operating while the precipitation is developing. With the passage of time, the cloud reaches altitudes where temperatures are cold enough for ice particles to form. During the same period, the electrification process may have been acting steadily to produce the quantities of charges leading to lightning.

In view of the questions about the requirements for ice particles, it is not surprising that there are several theories for cloud electrification. As a matter of fact, we can conveniently divide the most plausible ones into two groups—those that require ice particles and those that do not.

It has long been known that the atmosphere contains minute charged particles called "ions." They are in the form of gas molecules and dust particles. The theories of electrification, which specify that ice is not necessary, involve the capture of ions by cloud and raindrops. This idea was first proposed in 1929 by an English scientist, C. T. R. Wilson. He visualized that in an existing electric field such as the one found in the early stages of cloud growth, larger droplets would capture the negative ions. The positive ones would be carried to the upper parts of the cloud by the updraft. B. J. Mason at Imperial College, London, has argued that this process cannot separate charge fast enough. His view has been disputed by various authorities. In particular, Bernard Vonnegut and Charles

B. Moore of A. D. Little, Inc., have taken the position that there is observational evidence that a process such as the one proposed by Wilson can account for the necessary charging rates. They have further argued that the electrification not only precedes the formation of precipitation, but also leads to an acceleration of the growth of precipitation particles.

During the middle fifties, Ross Gunn at the Weather Bureau performed extensive research on various mechanisms of ion capture by cloud droplets. He concluded that under a variety of cloud conditions, so-called "ionic charging" could account for the electric charges observed on droplets in thunderstorms.

As we have already noted, a large group of scientists regard the processes of ionic charging as secondary to those involving ice. In the late thirties, G. C. Simpson in England proposed that the collision of ice crystals leads to the separation of positive and negative charge and was important in the electrification process. This process does in fact lead to charge separation, but the quantities are too small to account for thunderstorm charging.

Very convincing evidence of the importance of ice particles in the generation of electric charge was first obtained at the New Mexico Institute of Mining and Technology by E. J. Workman and his colleagues, Stephen E. Reynolds and Marx Brook. Through a long series of laboratory experiments, they clearly demonstrated that ice particles in a cloud make it possible to separate large quantities of charge. Their early work showed, that as water freezes, the ice usually is negative and the water is positive. They proposed a thunderstorm charging process based on these findings. When supercooled water droplets strike a frozen particle, they start to freeze. If the air flowing around the particle carries away some of the water before it freezes, the ice particle will be left with a negative charge. The small water fragments, charged positively, would be lifted to the upper parts of the cloud by the updraft. One of the difficulties with this scheme is that the electrical effects depend to an important extent on the impurities in the water. Further study also showed that the freezing process in New Mexico thunderclouds probably does not proceed in the manner required by the theory. For these reasons, additional experiments were performed during the middle fifties.

The New Mexico group conducted laboratory experiments to find out what happens when an ice crystal collides with a small "soft" hailstone.* It was found that when two pieces of ice are brought into momentary contact, charge is separated, providing the temperatures of the pieces of ice differ. The warmer one becomes negative, the colder one positive. In thunderstorms, small hail particles are likely to be warmer than surrounding ice crystals. As a result, the hailstones become negative while the rebounding ice crystals acquire a positive charge. The hailstones fall to the middle and lower regions of the cloud, and the small ice crystals are carried up to the cloud summits. The New Mexico scientists concluded that this mechanism separated sufficient charge to account for observed thunderstorm charging rates.

In 1961, the English scientists J. Latham and B. J. Mason published results of experiments that support, to a certain extent, the earlier work just discussed. However, they proposed that an effective charging mechanism occurs when supercooled droplets collide with a small, soft hailstone. They visualize that freezing of the droplets is accompanied by the ejection of tiny, positively charged ice splinters. Objections to this hypothesis have been raised on the grounds that such a process would lead to far more ice crystals than are observed.

In summary, we should point out that laboratory experiments and observations in the free atmosphere strongly support the idea that ice particles play an important role in the formation of thunderstorm electrification. On the other hand, the literature does contain some reports of lightning in clouds in which ice crystals were unlikely to be present. The clouds in question were over tropical oceans and of the type in which rain usually forms with-

---

* A soft hailstone or snow pellet is a particle of ice composed of many ice crystals. Instead of being a solid piece of ice, it is more nearly like a miniature snowball. It is easily crushed, and bounces when it strikes the ground. Diameters of a few sixteenths of an inch are common.

out the presence of ice crystals. Questions have been raised about the validity of these few scattered observations, but there are not adequate grounds for completely rejecting them.

As has already been suggested by a number of scientists, perhaps there is more than one effective mechanism by which large convective clouds can be electrified. We know that there are two chief processes for the formation of precipitation—one involves ice crystals, the other does not. Until more research is done, it will not be possible to state categorically whether or not the same holds true for the formation of large charged regions in thunderstorms.

Observing lightning

The signature of a thunderstorm is the brilliant streak of light known since the dawn of time. When it strikes the ground, it literally scorches the earth. Lightning starts an average of about 7,500 forest fires in the United States every year. The cost is high—about $25,000,000 annually. Precious timber, which takes decades to grow, is converted into piles of ashes. Then, too, there is tremendous loss of wildlife. Areas whose beauty is the source of great pleasure may be scarred and destroyed in a matter of hours or days. (See Plate IX).

As we all know, lightning does not restrict itself to forests. It also strikes houses and people. During the 10-year period ending in 1958, an average of 180 persons per year were electrocuted by lightning in the United States. This is not a large number when compared with the fatalities caused by diseases such as cancer or the steady massacre of the automobile (more than 100 per day in the U.S.). Nevertheless, to the unfortunate survivors of a strike victim, statistics offer little comfort. Lightning fatalities are tragic in many ways. Fortunately, most of them can be avoided by staying in your house or automobile when a storm approaches. One of the worst places to seek cover is under a tree. This point is made time and again by meteorologists, but every year people go under trees to avoid getting wet and are electrocuted. Tall, isolated trees are favored lightning targets.

For many centuries, little was known about lightning besides the facts that it was bright, hot, left a slight lingering odor, and lasted only a very short time. Important discoveries awaited the development of fast-responding cameras and electronic devices.

The first major step forward was made in 1902 by Charles Boys in England. He conceived a camera to record the rapidly changing events during a lightning stroke. Although Boys did not succeed in getting any really satisfactory pictures, his ideas served as a basis for further developments. In 1933, B. F. J. Schonland in South Africa constructed a camera based on the original Boys instrument. It worked very well indeed and supplied valuable observations of the evolution of cloud-to-ground lightning strokes.

During the intervening years, much more elaborate and expensive camera equipment has been designed and built. In order to get information about the movement of a lightning stroke, the Boys camera employs two lenses rotating rapidly about a horizontal axis. Alternately one can hold the lens fixed and move the film. Pairs of photographs are taken in quick succession. By comparing the photographs, you can learn various facts. Nowadays, there are cameras for taking photographs at rates exceeding 25,000 frames per second. Only recently have atmospheric physicists begun to use them in lightning studies. For this reason, much of what we know about visual lightning has come from studies made by various types of Boys cameras. We can look forward to more detailed information about lightning as the new equipment becomes more widely used.

Over the last 20 years, electronic measurements have been a major source of information about lightning storms. Photographically, it is very difficult to separate events occurring within a few millionths of a second of one another. This is certainly not the case with electronic techniques. Since the luminous events associated with lightning are caused by the presence and movement of electric charges, these events can be studied indirectly by measuring the electric fields and their changes.

When a lightning stroke occurs, it generates radio waves. The static we hear on ordinary radios during a lightning storm is an example of the type of signal produced. They are called "sferics," from the term "atmospherics." By recording the sferic signals and analyzing the records, we can learn about the buildup and decay of lightning discharges.

We now know that accompanying lightning strokes there are electrical streamers whose light intensity is too small to be seen with conventional cameras. They are easily detected electronically. In addition, movements of charges inside the cloud cannot be seen visually or photographically. Again, electronic techniques come to the rescue and allow us to infer what goes on.

Lightning strikes

Lightning strokes can be divided into two broad categories—cloud-to-ground and cloud-to-cloud. The first category is of the most practical importance for the reasons already mentioned.

Cloud-to-cloud strokes are, simply, all those strokes not reaching the ground. They must be understood and explained if we are to have a complete picture of a thunderstorm. They also have some practical importance. Airplanes are often hit by lightning flashes that start and end in the same cloud. We should here note that such events are much more frightening than dangerous. Modern commercial and military airplanes are virtually immune from serious damage by a direct lightning strike. When they are struck, there is a brilliant flash of light and a loud noise; the airplane may bounce, but the effects are usually minor. It is common to have small holes a few tenths of an inch in diameter burned in a wing surface. Sometimes a radio antenna is burned off. Perhaps a pitot tube is fused. However, these types of damage and others like them are not of a major nature. They do not affect the flight characteristics of the airplane. Experienced pilots take these situations in stride.

Let us return to the cloud-to-ground stroke and see how it develops. The reason it occurs is known. It is a means of relieving the "electrical tension" in the cloud. As the electrification process proceeds and the stored

94

charge becomes progressively larger, the electric field between the cloud and the ground grows more intense. When it approaches about 300,000 volts/foot in the presence of water droplets, the air "breaks down." It no longer can prevent the charges in the cloud from starting to flash toward the ground.

Detailed investigations have made it clear that lightning is not a single sudden surge of electrical charge. Instead, there is a series of processes.

At the beginning, there occurs the so-called "stepped leader." It originates in the thunderstorm and makes its way toward the ground. Schonland proposed that it follows closely behind a "pilot streamer." He visualized the latter as being caused when the electric field becomes strong enough to accelerate free electrons in the base of the cloud to speeds of about 90 mi/sec. Since the lower region of the cloud is strongly negative, it exerts a strong downward repelling force on the negative electrons. When this occurs, they collide with air molecules and cause the formation of ions. An avalanche of electrons may cause an ionized channel some 50 yards long and perhaps 4 inches in diameter. The presence of the ions makes the air more conductive, and electric charges flow freely down the first step in the ionized path.

Observations have shown that a stepped leader does in fact occur. The pilot streamer is too weak to give sufficient light to be photographed, but the stepped leader can be followed. It moves downward an average of about 50 yards in about one microsecond (a millionth of a second). It then pauses for a period of 50 to 100 microseconds and then takes another 50-yard jump downward. This sequence of events is repeated until the leader gets close to the ground. A period of perhaps a hundredth of a second is required for the leader to progress from cloud to ground. When it is within perhaps 10 to 50 yards from the earth, it attracts charged ions upward. At the joining of the downward and upward surges of electric charge, the so-called "return stroke" occurs. It represents the high point of the lightning stroke. A massive quantity of charge moves through the channel and produces the sudden brilliant emission of light we all know so well.

When tall, isolated trees or buildings are present, the downward streamer has a shorter distance to travel before joining the upward surge of charge. As a result, these objects are much more often struck by lightning than are lower plants and structures.

Although the term *return stroke* is a common one, it is somewhat misleading. Photographs show that the luminous tip moves up the channel, but the electric charges actually move down. Just before the stepped leader reaches the earth, the electrified channel contains huge numbers of ions. The air normally has about 10^5 ions per cubic centimeter. But in the stepped-leader channel, the number is about 10^{16} ions per cubic inch. As soon as the leader makes electrical contact with the ground, the ions begin to drain rapidly out of the channel. The lowest ones come down first; then they cascade down from higher and higher levels. The brilliant tip of the return likewise propagates higher and higher until it penetrates the cloud.

The return stroke moves up its narrow path at about one tenth the speed of light. Measurements show that the luminous channel is only a few inches in diameter. During the 40 to 50 microseconds of its existence, tremendous electrical currents are produced. The largest values of current occur shortly after the cloud is short-circuited to the ground. About 10 microseconds after the start of the return stroke, the current may frequently be as much as 30,000 amperes, but sometimes may exceed 200,000 amperes. The current falls off more slowly than it builds up. After about 25 microseconds, it may be about half its maximum value.

During the past few years, estimates have been made of the temperature of the lightning channel. This has been done by observing the optical spectrum of lightning. The light from a group of strokes or from an individual stroke has been collected, separated into its various color components from red to ultraviolet, and recorded with special cameras. By detailed studies of photographic prints of individual strokes, scientists led by Leon E. Salanave at the University of Arizona have found that the temperature averages about 45,000°F. This value is in fair agreement with estimates made in

1960 by L. Wallace of the University of Chicago and by two Russian scientists in 1961. In view of the very high temperatures, it is no wonder that trees or houses may be set instantly ablaze.

By the time the return stroke is finished, a large number of charges have been removed from the lightning channel. They are not all removed, however; many still remain. They are in the form of negatively charged electrons and positively charged oxygen and nitrogen molecules. As soon as the lightning current becomes small, the electrons begin to recombine with the positive molecules. While this is going on, the channel is still a good conductor of electricity. Most often, before the ions do very much recombining, a second lightning flash occurs in the same channel.

Because a conductive path already exists, it is not necessary for the stepped-leader process to take place again. Instead, a so-called "dart leader" flashes from cloud to ground at a speed of about one hundredth the speed of light. As soon as it reaches the surface, another powerful return stroke takes place.

Sometimes this chain of events repeats itself time and again. At intervals of a few hundredths of a second, as many as 40 or more return strokes may occur. Of course, these are extreme cases, but it is not unusual to have 5 to 10 flashes. All of them move down the same channel. The human eye certainly cannot distinguish one return flash from the next. On the other hand, a lightning stroke that lasts for the best part of a second clearly can be recognized as an unusual one. Some observers have said such strokes appear to flicker or "sizzle." This is presumably caused by the fact that the light emitted reaches intermittent high and low intensities. Also, the return flashes do not follow precisely the same path. From one flash to the next there may be minor shifts of position.

The occurrence of multiple-flash lightning has been known for quite a few years—Schonland noted it in the late 1930's, for instance—but recently it has been getting additional study. Marx Brook and his colleagues at the New Mexico Institute of Mining and Technology have employed modern photographic and electronic techniques to observe cloud-to-ground lightning. They found that about 90 percent of the strokes in New Mexico were of the multiple-flash variety. This is considerably higher than the 50 percent reported in England by C. E. R. Bruce and R. H. Golde in 1942. It is likely that the discrepancy is a reflection of real differences in lightning storms in two such widely separated regions as New Mexico and England. The two places are not only geographically diverse, they are also almost climatological opposites.

The scientists in New Mexico found that the individual flashes in multiple-flash lightning follow at intervals of from about a hundredth to a tenth of a second. When a period of more than a tenth of a second elapses, the next return stroke from a particular thunderstorm is likely to follow a different path. This result indicates that in a tenth of a second the recombination of ions in the channel is well advanced—so much so that the electrified channel no longer exists.

Brook and colleagues also found another important feature of lightning flashes—the return stroke is sometimes in the form of a short pulse of intense current. It starts fast and ends fast. In other cases, the strokes die slowly. The current builds rapidly to a peak but drops off gradually. The current continues to flow for several tenths of a second. Sometimes it lasts for as much as half a second. The diminishing but persistent current results in a correspondingly long period of faintly luminous lightning channel.

When a thunderstorm produces only a single return stroke, it is almost always of short duration. But the later, and particularly the last flash, of a multiple-flash stroke is a lingering one. It appears that in this process the last flash acts to tap the last residue of cloud charge and drain it to ground.

The question of why some strokes are composed of only a single flash while others have a rapid fire of from 2 to over 40 flashes still has not been satisfactorily resolved. Although it has been proposed that the thunderstorm may regenerate electric charge fast enough to produce many strokes at short time intervals, this suggestion seems very unlikely. It is difficult enough to explain the charging in a matter of minutes, much less a fraction of a second.

The most plausible reason for multiple flashes seems to be that most thunderstorms contain many discrete regions of concentrated electrical charges. A strongly charged region close to the ground makes initial contact with the surface via the stepped-leader and the main stroke. Then other charge centers can be successively discharged to the ground via the old charge center and ionized channel. Schonland proposed that by a series of steps, charge centers higher and higher in the cloud can be discharged by means of new dart leaders and main strokes. Clearly, the question of the reason for multiple-flash strokes needs to be settled through further research.

Over the years, particular types of lightning strokes have been given special names. In general, they have been given by laymen rather than scientists. In most cases, the names refer to the appearance and do not reflect a fundamental difference in the lightning mechanism. For example, when the wind is strong, the ionized cloud-to-ground channel moves horizontally at a rapid rate. If a multiple-flash stroke occurs, the individual flashes are displaced sidewise. When this occurs, it is sometimes called "ribbon lightning."

Occasionally a stepped-leader forms branches before it reaches the ground. As a result, the return stroke moves up two or more separate paths before joining the main channel into the cloud. The term "forked lightning" is commonly given in such cases.

In certain instances, cloud-to-cloud lightning has been given particular names. For example, lightning may occur so far away that the thunder cannot be heard even though the light can be seen. When it is scattered and reflected by cloud drops, large regions of the sky can be illuminated. The name "heat lightning" has been given to this lightning.

Sometimes at dusk and at night, lightning occurs inside clouds. The strokes may extend for many miles. Cloud droplets and ice crystals obscure the brilliant bolt from direct view and also scatter and diffuse the light so that a large region of the cloud is illuminated. This is called "sheet lightning." Sometimes thunder is heard, but at other times the discharge is too far away and the sound escapes detection. To the eye, sheet lightning certainly looks different from a flash of lightning between two clouds separated by blue sky. However, there is no reason for believing that the basic discharge mechanisms are different. In one case, we see the flash directly; in the other, the flash is masked by a diffuse screen of water and ice particles.

An interesting and unusual sight is "bead lightning." We still are not sure if this phenomenon is basically different from ordinary lightning. In rare instances, the luminous channel of a stroke does not dissolve from sight uniformly along the path. Instead, it breaks up into discrete sections of light and dark regions. The luminous parts, reported to be some tens of yards long, give the appearance of a string of beads. Of course, the entire process from lightning flash to formation of beads to complete disappearance takes only a second or less. Nevertheless, the beaded appearance is quite clear.

It has been suggested that the obviously beaded appearance does not mean that certain portions of the stroke are brighter than others. A distant stroke could give such an impression if certain portions in a bending, twisting stroke are viewed directly down the channel. Even if the section of channel in line with the eye is small, it still would have more luminosity than would the channel when viewed from the sides. Although we still cannot reject this explanation, another intriguing one has been put forth recently. The new explanation carries the inference that the bright beads are actually regions giving off more intense light. Martin A. Uman and Walter H. Evans at the University of Arizona have proposed that they are caused by a process called the "pinch effect."

Laboratory experiments and theoretical calculations show that when a narrow channel carries very large currents, they set up magnetic fields that lead to a pinching of the channel. In very special circumstances, the pinching occurs at intervals down the channel. At the places where the narrowing occurs, there should be an intensification of the brightness. This proposal is certainly interesting, but it is still in the stage of an untested hypothesis.

One of the most fascinating types of electrical discharge observed in the vicinity of thunderstorms is "ball lightning." Until about 10 years ago, there was serious doubt that such a thing actually existed. However, the number of observations by qualified observers has increased to the point that its validity is generally accepted.

Ball lightning is described as a roughly spherical region of luminous air. Reported diameters have ranged from several inches to several yards; 10 inches is taken as a typical value. Durations of the bright balls may be from several seconds to several minutes. Sometimes they silently dissolve. On other occasions, they disappear with an explosive sound, but they usually do little if any physical damage. Occasionally they leave behind the smell of ozone.

Witnesses have ascribed an almost ghostly quality to the "fireball," as it is sometimes called. It may float gently along, through screened doors and windows, through cracks in doors, or down a fireplace chimney. There have been reports of ball lightning passing into and out of the same room without touching or harming anyone or anything.

Ball lightning occurs in the presence of a lightning storm. For this reason, one must look to the thunderstorm electric charges and lightning for an explanation. Various hypotheses have been offered. One that explains some of the known properties was offered in 1955 by the Russian scientist P. L. Kapitza. He proposed that the energy for the luminous ball comes from the radio waves produced by lightning strokes. He suggested that these waves can lead to the glow of atmospheric gases in the manner that neon lamps glow.

A later hypothesis has been put forward by E. L. Hill at the University of Minnesota. He proposes that some cloud-to-ground lightning strokes may lead to unusually high concentrations of charged gas molecules in small regions near the ground. As the ions in the volume recombine and as the most heavily charged one gives off excess charge, light is emitted. It is not evident that ion concentrations of the required size and composition are

101

actually produced. Hill has argued that his hypothesis can explain the durations of several seconds. It appears that Kapitza's does not.

It is obvious that there are still some fundamental questions about ball lightning without satisfactory answers. The hypotheses proposed by Kapitza, Hill, and others do not satisfactorily explain all the known and suspected features of ball lightning. We say "suspected" because very few *measurements* exist. Most information has come from people who happened to be at the same place as the fireball. If more were known about it, we might be able to predict where and when ball lightning will occur. Then appropriate instruments could be used for making measurements.

Present research on this problem is not solely concerned with interpreting secondhand observations and constructing theoretical models. Attempts are being made to produce artificial ball lightning in a laboratory. When these experiments are successful, a great step forward will have been made in understanding the mysterious fireball.

Thunder

It is common to speak of lightning as if it were a giant electric spark or arc. In describing thunder, various authors have compared it to an explosion.

As we already mentioned, the massive surge of electric current may heat up the channel to perhaps 40,000 to 50,000°F in a small fraction of a second. This leads to a sudden expansion of the air and the production of sound waves. They propagate outward in all directions at a speed of about 1,100 feet per second. As they move farther away from the source, they weaken rapidly.

Before going on, we should note that it has been suggested that, in some cases, the first stage in thunder generation is compression rather than expansion. This seems impossible in the light of the very high temperatures of the lightning, but let us consider how it might happen. It is proposed that the magnetic field produced at the time of peak current leads to a pinching of the channel. This is the same effect we noted as a possible explanation for bead lightning. The pinching is said to lead to a sudden and momentary contraction followed by rapid expansion as the sound wave is produced.

Unfortunately, the number of measurements of the properties of thunder is small. The most extensive ones were made in 1913 by a German scientist, Wilhelm Schmidt, and more recently in Russia by V. I. Arabadzhi. These men recorded the sound frequencies and the pressure variations associated with the sound waves.

The existing measurements are difficult to interpret for various reasons. First of all, you need precise information about the equipment employed. In order to obtain reliable data about the sound frequencies and their intensities, high-fidelity detection and recording equipment must be used. If this is not done, the equipment will distort the records. The second difficulty involved in recording and analyzing thundery sounds is the fact that sound waves have different properties in different places.

Just before lightning strikes nearby, you sometimes hear a "click." This noise is a sign that the stepped-leader has just about made contact with the ground stroke. The actual sound is ascribed to the upward rush of charges on their way to meet the downward leader. Once the return stroke occurs, the characteristics of the sound waves reaching a listener depend not only on the strength of the current surge, but also on the listener's distance from the stroke, its orientation in space, and its shape. The wind velocity, temperature variations in the atmosphere, and the character of the terrain all influence the sound reaching the human ear or the microphone on a recorder.

In order to avoid some of these difficulties, you obviously have to take many kinds of observations. Suitable photographs can indicate the location, shape, and orientation of the lightning stroke. Standard weather instruments can measure the properties of the atmosphere. Even if these were available along with suitable thunder-recording equipment, you need still one more thing—patience. Once you have set up all the apparatus, you must

103

wait until lightning occurs within the observing range of all the instruments.

Such an approach to the study of thunder still has not been successfully employed, largely because other interesting problems of atmospheric physics have attracted talented scientists. However, it is anticipated that before long this relatively neglected problem will get more attention.

We do know some things about thunder. For example, one can usually hear thunder if the lightning channel is less than about 10 miles away. If the air is still, or if the wind is blowing from the storm toward you, it is possible to hear thunder generated perhaps 20 miles away. The light produced in the lightning channel can be seen from much greater distances. In dry regions, such as the southwestern United States, where the air is quite transparent, you can see lightning from a range of more than 50 miles.

When a lightning stroke is seen and its thunder heard, you can make a good estimate of its distance. Since the speed of light is 186,000 miles per second, the light from a stroke 186 miles away arrives in a thousandth of a second. For purposes of estimation, you can consider the light to be seen the instant it occurs. On the other hand, sound travels slowly—1 mile in about 5 seconds. Therefore, if you count the seconds between the sighting of the lightning and the time of thunder, you can easily judge the distance to the stroke. Allow 1 mile for every 5 seconds of elapsed time. This scheme works only if the lightning strokes are fairly isolated and at some distance from the observer. Nearly vertical, cloud-to-ground strokes some 2 to 6 miles away can be positioned with good accuracy.

When a lightning channel follows a twisting, horizontal path across the sky before hitting the ground, you cannot talk about "the distance to the stroke"—you have to specify a particular part of the stroke. A channel may pass directly overhead at the height of 1 mile and then strike the ground 2 miles away (see Figure 15). Sound is generated along the entire length at almost the same instant. You first hear the noise from the closest point— namely, from overhead. Then sound waves come in from

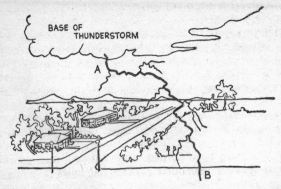

Figure 15.   *A lightning channel passes about one mile directly overhead and then strikes the ground two miles away. Sound waves are generated all along the path. The waves from directly overhead (A) arrive in 5 seconds, those from the ground (B) take 10 seconds, while waves from intermediate points take intermediate times. The result is thunder rumbling for 5 seconds.*

successively greater distances out to a maximum of 2 miles. As a result, the thunder may start off with a loud crack followed by a rumbling sound. In our example, the rumble lasts for about 5 seconds.

The roll of thunder may also be caused in other ways. In mountainous regions, the sound waves can be reflected from the high land and produce an echoing effect.

At times the thunderstorms may be so numerous that several lightning strokes from different storms occur in rapid succession. The sound waves may combine and interfere to cause a rumbling sensation.

In 1960, Wilfred J. Remillard at Harvard proposed that long rolls of thunder may be caused by reflection of sound waves from the upper parts of the thundercloud. He concluded from his studies that a layer of ice pellets near the top of the lightning channel can effectively reflect the sound waves. Thus, when lightning occurs, we hear first the direct waves and then the reflected ones. Since the same effect may happen with the sound waves from many parts of the channel, a rumbling, prolonged sound is heard.

Sometimes a lightning discharge is too far away to be heard even though it is seen. But most of the time, where there is lightning, there is thunder. However, there have been reports of lightning with no sound. It is possible that, in very special cases, the electrical discharge takes place at a slow rate. Instead of the tremendous surge of the return stroke, there may be a longer, but low current transfer of charge. In such an event, a luminous channel is produced, but the heating takes place slowly. As a result, the expansion of the channel is not nearly as rapid as in the case of the more normal return stroke. Such instances may occur with cloud-to-ground discharges to very tall buildings or with discharges within clouds.

Clearly, there are many things we still have to learn about thunder.

7

TAMING THE STORM

As long as man regarded thunderstorms as tools of the gods, they were accepted as violent, but probably appropriate ways to punish the wayward. In a fiery instant, a man and his possessions could be totally destroyed.

With the enlightened realization that thunderstorms were part of nature's grand scheme, the attitude of acceptance began to change. The men we now call scientists accumulated facts. They tabulated observations: Where does lightning strike most often? How does it look? How long does it last? When do storms produce torrential rains and hail? When does the thunder occur? And so forth. The reasoning was straightforward. Learn the facts about thunderstorms. Then perhaps it would be possible to devise defenses.

The most feared aspect of a thunderstorm was, and probably still is, lightning. It burns and it electrocutes. Benjamin Franklin and other contemporary scholars pointed their efforts toward finding an effective means of protection against lightning. Franklin's success is well known. He became a great hero in his own time by inventing the lightning rod. His experiments showed that lightning was an electrical discharge. He reasoned that when it struck the top of a house or a church steeple, favorite targets because of their heights, the electrical currents passed through them and produced very high temperatures. Wooden structures would be set aflame. Buildings of stone were badly damaged because the great heat caused them to fall apart. Water vapor and air trapped in between the bricks and stones expanded rapidly when heated and exerted sufficient pressure to blow the structures apart.

Franklin concluded that the way to protect buildings was to divert the electric currents around, rather than let them pass through, the structure. His idea is quite simple. Pointed metal rods are mounted at the highest parts of the roofs and pointed upward. Metal conductors in the form of metal rods or heavy cables are then connected to the rod and strung outside the building to other metal rods driven into the ground. When a thunderstorm passes overhead and sends one of its flashes toward the building, the rods are waiting. Because they extend to a higher level than the housetop, the lightning strikes the rods. The surge of electric charge passes down the cable and into the ground. In so doing, the current avoids passing through the building. The lightning rods get hot. Sometimes parts may even be melted by extremely large currents. But the house is protected.

Since Franklin's days, the use of lightning rods has become widespread. In principle, the ones used today are identical with the ones he proposed. They have done a good job. They have not completely eliminated the hazards of lightning, however; it still causes millions of dollars of damage every year, particularly in forest fires.

As was noted in earlier chapters, thunderstorms are also destructive in nonelectrical ways. Hail causes widespread crop devastation every year. The wheat lands of the Great Plains, especially in Nebraska, Kansas, and Colorado, are favorite breeding grounds for hail. Many rich fruitgrowing regions throughout the world periodically suffer catastrophic losses. Since the middle forties, serious attempts have been made to suppress damaging hail. So far the results have not been very encouraging, but the search goes on. In a later section, we will say more about this problem.

Another weapon of the thunderstorm is the "flash flood." Torrential rains can make narrow streams overflow their banks in a few hours. Although sudden flooding can occur almost anywhere, the most serious hazards are found in the more arid regions of the world—in southern New Mexico and Arizona, for instance. In these regions, many river and creek beds are completely dry for most of the year. The vegetation is sparse, and the soil often is not porous. Coupled with these factors is the mountain and valley topography.

An intense thunderstorm rainfall lasting for a period of an hour or so can lead to the very rapid filling of the creeks and rivers. Since the storms are most likely to form over the higher terrain, the water on the ground immediately drains into the stream beds. Little water is absorbed into the ground. The vegetation is inadequate to slow down the drainage. As a result, the streams can be filled with rushing, turbulent water very quickly.

Every year children and even adults are caught in river or creek beds and carried to their deaths. Sometimes roads are crossed by the water surging toward lower land. Automobiles are swept off the roads and become like corks in the torrent. On some occasions, the water seriously floods fields planted with irrigated crops.

It is unfortunate that the rate of rainfall from some thunderstorms is so excessive. For many areas, thunderstorm precipitation represents the difference between prosperity and ruin. The lives of many millions of people depend on convective rains. Because of its importance, we want thunderstorms of light, moderate, and even heavy intensity to continue to bring the beneficial rains on which we depend so much. However, we also would like to exert sufficient control so as to reduce the occurence of extremely heavy and destructive storms. There have been serious attempts to accomplish this aim.

Modifying thunderstorms

Franklin devised a scheme for protecting buildings from lightning. Over the 200 years since his monumental work, there have been sporadic attempts to do more than protect—people have wanted to modify and control. If you could prevent the development of large charge centers, you would not need lightning rods because there would be no lightning. Of course, the big question is, how do you control the storms?

Even before Franklin, primitive peoples had special dances and rituals to implore the gods to ward off the violent storm. In more recent centuries, there have been other schemes. One of the favorites was firing cannons, presumably on the grounds that the sound waves would have some effects. Other ideas involved the shooting of sand and other particles into clouds. One of the chief difficulties with early attempts to modify clouds was that very little was known about natural storm processes. To a lesser extent, this is still true. Unless you understand the nature of the phenomenon reasonably well, it is difficult to change it predictably.

The foundation of attempts to control thunderstorms was laid during the period 1930 to 1946. Our knowledge of convective clouds and the mechanisms of precipitation increased materially.

In the early thirties, the Norwegian meteorologist Tor Bergeron presented a new theory on precipitation. It stated that in order for precipitation to form, there must be ice crystals and water drops at temperatures below freezing. In 1946, Irving Langmuir and Vincent J. Schaefer at General Electric Laboratories tested this idea. They performed experiments demonstrating that *shallow layers* of supercooled clouds (water clouds at temperatures below 32°F) could be modified. They produced ice crystals in supercooled clouds by dropping pellets of dry ice (solid carbon dioxide). As predicted by the theory, the ice crystals grew and fell out of the cloud. The experiments were successfully performed many times.

The completion of these tests may be regarded as the start of major attempts to modify storms. Since that time, attention has been given to reducing cloud-to-ground lightning, suppressing damaging hail, and preventing torrential rainfall.

Changing the charges

As has already been noted, before attempting to change the electrical properties of thunderstorms, you

110

should have some firm ideas on how nature does it. Earlier, we mentioned that a large number of scientists believe that the major charge-generating process involves the interaction of small ice pellets and either supercooled droplets or ice crystals. It has been reasoned that if the upper part of a convective cloud were composed entirely of ice crystals, charge generation would be greatly reduced. This being the case, lightning would be prevented.

Ice crystals can be produced by seeding supercooled clouds with dry ice or certain types of minutely divided chemicals. A common one is silver iodide, which has been dispersed by means of rockets, balloons, airplanes, and from the ground. In almost all cases, the chemical is subjected to very high temperatures that vaporize the substance. As the vapor is cooled, tiny silver-iodide crystals are formed. Their diameters are from 0.01 to 1.0 micron. When they enter a water cloud at temperatures below about 20°F, ice crystals are produced. Tests to reduce cloud-to-ground lightning by means of cloud seeding have been made by various groups. None of the tests has yet succeeded in showing conclusively that lightning is less frequent on the days when the thunderstorms are seeded.

Because of the great variation of lightning occurrence from one thunderstorm situation to the next, it is difficult to find small effects. Perhaps the seeding actually did cause some, but the statistical techniques of analysis were unable to find them. On the other hand, it is likely that in most tests there were no effects at all. For the most part, the quantities of seeding material employed have been too small to convert almost all the supercooled cloud droplets to ice crystals. This condition, known as "overseeding," requires large amounts of dry ice or silver iodide. Even if the ice-water theories of thunderstorm electrification are correct, unless the cloud is overseeded, the chances of significantly altering its electrical properties are not good.

Those experts who say ice particles are not required for charge separation do not regard ice-crystal seeding techniques as promising. Instead, they maintain that it may be possible to modify convective clouds and thun-

111

derstorms by changing the ion properties of the air below the cloud.

Bernard Vonnegut and Charles Moore, who hold this view, have already demonstrated that the electrification of small convective clouds can be controlled. In cooperation with the Illinois State Water Survey, they stretched a fine electrified wire 8.7 miles long at a height of 33 feet over the level ground of central Illinois. By charging the wire to high voltages, they were able to modify the so-called "space charge" under the clouds. Electric charges escaped from the wire and attached themselves to air molecules and small dust and smoke particles in the air.

As convective clouds developed in the vicinity of the wire, low-level air moved up through the cloud in the updraft (see Figure 16). When the ions became at-

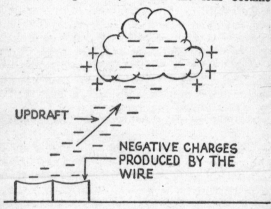

Figure 16. *A wire 8.7 miles long, charged with large negative voltage, produces negative charges. They are carried into the cloud by the updraft and become attached to the cloud droplets. The cloud becomes negatively charged. Some positive charges are found around the edges of the cloud near its base. By charging the wire positively, the cloud becomes charged positively.*

tached to the cloud droplets, the cloud became charged electrically. The experiments showed that the sign of the electrical charge on the clouds was determined by the

112

sign of the charge released by the wire. When a negative charge was produced, the cloud became negatively charged, and vice versa.

The clear-cut results of these experiments have led Vonnegut and Moore to conclude not only that convective cloud charging can be changed, but also that the principle convective-cloud-charging mechanism in nature is one involving ion capture. They are quick to point out that one cannot simply extend the results to include thunderstorms. Nevertheless, they recognize that this may in fact be true and are currently engaged in further research on this question.

Suppressing damaging hail

For the last 10 to 15 years, farmers in Italy and other European countries have been employing rockets in attempts to suppress the incidence of damaging hail. The rockets reach altitudes of about 3,000 to 5,000 feet, where almost 1 pound of gunpowder explodes. In practice, the firing begins when the threatening storms begin to pass over the farm with suitable armament. Once started, a substantial bombardment ensues. In 1959, the Italians fired about 100,000 rockets at passing thunderstorms.

The scientific basis for the rocket firings is not evident. Nevertheless, many farmers are convinced that they do reduce hail damage. The Italian scientist Ottavio Vittori has interviewed a large number of rocket users. He found that many of them said that shortly after the rocket firings, the hailstones became "mushy." Instead of breaking leaves and branches as they did when composed of solid ice, the stones squashed and fell apart upon contact.

To date no one has yet collected any of the so-called "mushy" hailstones or even taken careful observations as they fell to the ground. Thus the assertion that such stones actually occur following rocket firings still has not been conclusively established or rejected.

Vittori offered a possible hypothesis for the softening of the stones by the warhead explosions. He suggested

113

that the pressure wave set up could lead to tiny cracks as a result of the pressure effects on trapped water and air inside the stones. Some experiments he performed showed that stones quite close to the explosion could be so modified. However, other tests have indicated that the effects fall off rapidly with increasing distance between the exploding warhead and the hailstones.

In summary, we can say that although the widespread use of rockets with exploding nose cones continues, no one knows for sure whether or not they really do suppress damaging hail, and if they do, why they do.

Extensive work has been done to modify hailstorms by seeding them with ice-crystal nuclei. In most cases, silver iodide has been used for nuclei production. Seeding has been carried out from the ground, from airplanes, and by means of small rockets of the type designed by the Italians.

We mentioned in Chapter 4 that in order for hailstones to form, supercooled cloud droplets are needed. Cloud seeding with ice nuclei is aimed at reducing the quantity of supercooled water. However, in order for this scheme to have a reasonable chance for success, it is necessary to overseed the cloud—at least, this is the conclusion one would reach from a consideration of our present ideas on hailstorms.

To date no one has demonstrated conclusively that cloud seeding can reduce the fall of damaging hail. When you realize that the quantities of silver iodide dispensed have almost always been far short of the quantity needed for overseeding, perhaps this result is not surprising. In order to overseed large, hail-producing thunderstorms, the dosages of silver iodide would have to be 10 to 1,000 times greater than those used in the past. Since silver is an expensive metal, the costs of overseeding operations would exceed several thousands of dollars per cloud.

Presently, attempts are being made to find a less expensive chemical that is as good as silver iodide. When one is found, perhaps extensive overseeding tests will be performed.

In the meantime, research is continuing to establish a more concrete picture of how nature produces damaging hail. One has to admit the possibility that the model proposed in Chapter 4 is not correct. Continued research will lead not only to increased knowledge of the true nature of hailstorms, but also to a satisfactory scheme for modifying them.

Suppressing torrential rains

Attempts at suppressing torrential rains are based on the assumption that proper treatment can lead to smaller rainfall intensities for longer periods of time. Again, cloud seeding has been tried.

It has been argued that the introduction of large salt particles in the cloud bases will cause the formation of raindrops early in the cloud's life. If the drops become large enough, they may fall out of the updraft before they are carried to the higher parts of the clouds. If they reach high elevations where strong updrafts exist, they may be stored until the formation of the downdraft. At that time, tremendous quantities of precipitation can be dumped in a short time.

The idea that large salt particles can in fact frustrate the natural tendency of some clouds to produce torrential rains has not been adequately tested. We do not really know whether or not they will really do such a job.

Some attempts to prevent torrential rains have been based on the idea of overseeding. The Russian scientist A. P. Chuvayev has employed dry ice for this purpose and has reported some success, but details are lacking. In principle, overseeding should lead to the almost complete suppression of rainfall. Sometimes the net results of this effect, if it occurred, might be more damaging in the long run than the torrential rain would have been.

Summary

In the late forties, there was great optimism that we had finally found the keys to weather modification and control. Unfortunately, the keys have not yet opened many doors. It is quite true and has been well demonstrated that thin layers of supercooled clouds can be modified. The addition of ice nuclei leads to the formation of ice crystals large enough to fall out of the cloud. Sometimes they reach the ground.

In some cases, precipitation can be started in convective clouds. There is some evidence that in special situations it may be possible to produce increases in precipitation at the ground. However, this point has not yet been demonstrated beyond reasonable doubt.

The attempts to modify severe thunderstorms have been shown to be thus far unsuccessful. We have cited various techniques that have been tried; still others have been proposed. The lack of success can be ascribed in large part to the fact that there are many things we still do not know about thunderstorms. Until our knowledge of the properties and processes is further advanced, attempts at modification are not likely to succeed. It should be recognized, however, that properly conducted experiments, based on a reasonable hypothesis, are of value even when the results are negative. The experiment serves as a test of the validity of the hypothesis.

The optimism of scientists concerned with attempts to modify the weather has been somewhat dimmed the past few years, but it has not been extinguished. It still is reasonable to believe that increased understanding will lead to development of successful schemes for modification and control of thunderstorms.

8

THE PRESENT
AND THE FUTURE

Over the last 20 years we have learned many things about thunderstorms. In the process of learning, our ignorance has come more clearly into focus. Not so long ago we were asking vague questions. Now the questions can be formulated more precisely. We can construct hypotheses and test them.

Since the end of World War II, science and technology have made fantastic advances. High-speed electronic computers now allow us to solve problems of staggering complexity. Mountains of observational data can be handled with amazing rapidity.

Ingenious instruments for measuring the properties of the atmosphere have come into common use. Many kinds of radar equipment have been developed. We can detect cloud droplets, raindrops, snow crystals, and hail and measure their velocities. Lightning can be located and its properties recorded.

Elaborately instrumented airplanes, high-flying balloons, and weather satellites are in everyday use.

It appears that our ability to observe and digest weather behavior is equal to the task of unraveling the mysteries of thunderstorms. But there is still a serious drawback to rapid progress—there are not enough scientists working on thunderstorm problems.

The study of the atmospheric sciences in general, and thunderstorms in particular, is a fascinating and challenging one. Many points of fundamental importance deserve investigation. Imagination is needed—so is hard work.

The present

At the present time, research on all aspects of thunderstorms is in progress in many countries all over the world. For the most part, the various university and government projects are fairly modest in scope. One group is concentrating on the properties of lightning, another on hail, still another on the mechanism of cloud growth, and so forth. Each group is making its contribution to the overall knowledge. Slowly the picture is becoming clearer.

There has been one research program much greater than all the others. In 1960, the U. S. Weather Bureau formally organized the National Severe Storms Project —NSSP, for short. The project actually was started in 1956, when the Bureau employed the services of a single instrumented P-51 airplane owned and operated by James Cook of Jacksboro, Texas, for the purpose of collecting special observations in the vicinity of severe storms.

It soon became clear that in order to obtain the kind of observations required to describe severe storms, a much greater effort was needed.

By 1963 the program was impressive indeed. Other government agencies had joined the Weather Bureau in the NSSP. Several universities were active participants. The director, C. F. Van Thullenar, with the assistance of his chief scientist, Chester Newton, and the advice of other scientists, amassed an outstanding array of scientific gear. The Weather Bureau contributed two instrumented DC-6 airplanes for making a large variety of measurements in and around severe thunderstorms. An instrumented B-57 jet was employed for high-altitude observations.

The Air Force, the Federal Aviation Agency (FAA),
118

and the National Aeronautics and Space Administration (NASA) flew various types of jet airplanes in conjunction with the Weather Bureau aircraft. During the spring of 1961, a total of 13 aircraft made 107 flights.

All the groups involved in the NSSP are particularly interested in turbulence in the upper portions of large thunderstorms. Two NASA scientists, Roy Steiner and Richard H. Rhyne, have studied flight records collected during 1960 and 1961 by Air Force airplanes flying through thunderstorms at subsonic and supersonic speeds. They penetrated storms at 5,000-foot altitude intervals between 25,000 and 40,000 feet.

In the opening chapter of this book, we described thunderstorm flights made in 1947 by Air Force pilots in P-61 airplanes. It took courage then; it takes just as much courage today. When a jet flies through a mammoth thunderstorm at a speed of 600 mph, the turbulence may be extremely severe. The chances of losing part of the airplane are very real. Then, too, there is the possibility of hail. At jet speeds, the large stones can badly dent the airplane skin. If large stones are ingested into a jet engine, it can be quickly put out of commission.

Steiner and Rhyne concluded that vertical velocities as large as 200 ft/sec (136 mph) can exist in severe thunderstorms. Also, they reported that the turbulence at 40,000 feet was greater than that at lower altitudes.

The NSSP has employed much more than a fleet of airplanes. Weather-radar sets of the most advanced designs have been used for observing severe thunderstorms. During the spring of 1963, at least 6 different radar sets were operated in the vicinity of Oklahoma City. Coupled with this concentrated collection of radar equipment, there has been a dense network of other radar sets in the states surrounding Oklahoma.

In 1951, the Weather Bureau established a special network of surface weather stations located mostly in Texas, Oklahoma, and Kansas. By 1961, there were 200 ground-based automatic weather stations spaced about 30 miles apart. They have recorded pressure and most of them also measured temperature, humidity, and rainfall. Within this area, there has been a more concentrated

119

grid of 36 stations spaced 10 to 15 miles apart. They were equipped to measure the elements already mentioned plus wind velocity.

Finally, the NSSP has had available sounding equipment for measuring the vertical variations of pressure, temperature, and humidity by means of balloon-borne instruments. They have been used to fill in the gaps between the widely spaced permanent stations, normally taking only 2 balloon runs per day.

It is evident that an observational program of this magnitude accumulates data at a very great rate. Who has been analyzing it? Many different groups, governmental and private, have been involved in the study and interpretation.

The Future

Atmospheric scientists are looking hopefully to the measurements made by the National Severe Storms Project for answers to some of the important unsolved questions about thunderstorms. The observations should yield a better description of conditions in and around the storms. Careful analysis may allow us to discriminate between conflicting ideas on the development of the clouds, rain, hail, lightning, and tornadoes.

Perhaps the knowledge gained from this large project, coupled with that from the multitude of smaller ones, will allow us to formulate a comprehensive and realistic model of the thunderstorm. Of course, this is no ordinary job. It requires great scientific ability and the capacity to assemble a great many facts into a coherent whole. This is the challenge for the intellectual mountain climbers, whose satisfaction comes from solving the really difficult problems.

Once we more fully understand nature's design of thunderstorms, we should be able to devise schemes for modifying and controlling them. So far our efforts in this direction have not been successful, but this is not too surprising in view of the many uncertainties about the facts. When we learn the details of the chain of events leading to a violent thunderstorm, we should be able to

120

isolate the vulnerable links and take appropriate action. The enormous benefits accruing from success in this endeavor encourage us to greater efforts so that the time of its realization may not be too long delayed.

SUGGESTED READING

1. Nontechnical books dealing with thunderstorms:

L. J. Battan, *The Nature of Violent Storms.* Garden City, N.Y.: Doubleday & Co., Inc., 1961. 158 pp.

S. D. Flora, *Hailstorms of the United States.* Norman: University of Oklahoma Press, 1953. 194 pp.

B. F. J. Schonland, *The Flight of the Thunderbolts.* London: Oxford University Press, 1950. 152 pp.

2. More advanced books:

H. R. Byers (ed.), *Thunderstorm Electricity.* Chicago: University of Chicago Press, 1953. 344 pp.

H. R. Byers and R. R. Braham, Jr., *The Thunderstorm.* Washington, D. C.: U. S. Government Printing Office, 1949. 287 pp.

J. A. Chalmers, *Atmospheric Electricity.* London and New York: Pergamon Press, 1957. 327 pp.

N. H. Fletcher, *The Physics of Rainclouds.* London and New York: Cambridge University Press, 1961. 386 pp.

B. J. Mason, *The Physics of Clouds.* London and New York: Oxford University Press, 1957. 481 pp.

INDEX

123

125

126